THE LIFE AND TIMES OF WALTER MANN

Dedicated to working people wherever and whenever they find themselves

A novella by

Robert Teme

Matador
5 Weir Road
Kibworth Beauchamp
Leicester LE8 0LQ, UK
Tel: (+44) 116 279 2299
Fax: 0116 279 2277
Email: books@troubador.co.uk
Web: www.troubador.co.uk/matador

ISBN 978 1848761 377

British Library Cataloguing in Publication Data.
A catalogue record for this book is available from the British Library.

Typeset in 11pt Bembo by Troubador Publishing Ltd, Leicester, UK

Matador is an imprint of Troubador Publishing Ltd

Dedicated to working people wherever and whenever they find themselves

Acknowledgements

One of the best places to admire the magnificent Titterstone Clee Hill and its surroundings is from the high road along Whitcliffe Hill near Ludlow in Shropshire. St. Lawrence's Church, the River Teme and Ludlow Castle make a fine foreground for the 'bonk', as Titterstone is affectionately called locally. If your view is obscured by a cloud – 'Titterstone's got his hat on' – you should expect rain!

This book owes much to my father who, through his hard graft, made sure I had a good start in life. He also told me about his early years on the Clee Hills. Thanks are due to my mother who gave me some of her humility and, although she died more than ten years ago, still always makes me proud when I think of her. A glass too must be lifted to Alf Jenkins who was born on the bonk and, like me, attended Ludlow Grammar School. The photograph opposite page 46 of his wonderful tome '*Titterstone Clee Hills: Everyday Life, Industrial History and Dialect*', features a group of quarrymen just like Walter Mann, the main character of my book.

Then to Miss Ridgeway who worked at East Hamlet school in Ludlow and encouraged me to learn and to believe in myself, important for all children but most important for working class kids because of what they have to contend with.

Finally, to Tracey Chevalier and her *Falling Angels* for inspiration in terms of both content and method.

In order to protect family, friends and neighbours, names and details that might reveal identity have been changed in the text: as a result, any resemblance of the characters depicted to any person living or deceased is coincidental.

CHAPTER ONE

Pits and Poverty

I used to think 'Keir' was his first name but James Keir Hardie was the illegitimate son of Mary Keir, a servant from Legbrannock, Lanarkshire, Scotland. He was born on the 15th August 1856 and Mary later married David Hardie, the boy taking on both his parents' names. David, a ship's carpenter, was in and out of employment so that, at the age of eight, James had no option but to work, becoming a baker's delivery boy, working twelve and a half hours for a pittance. With his mother pregnant, James was the only bread-winner, so to speak. In the vicious winter of 1866, James' younger brother was dying and, after spending most of the night looking after him, the story goes that James was late for work. His employer was hard-pressed and, it seems, as ill-tempered a person as it was possible to meet so James got the sack and was fined a week's wages. At the age of eleven, he was a miner back in Lanarkshire, working a twelve hour day. He had never attended school and signed his name with a cross.

All this I record as a way of explaining the surprise I felt on discovering details about my own great grandmother's life. Like Mary, Catherine had a rural start in life before entering domestic service. She was born in Worcestershire, in 1857, so a generation on from Mary Keir. My family history had included a yarn about her having been well-to-do and ejected by her wealthy parents once they found out she was, with no small irony, in the 'family way'. Spurred on by snatches of Dickens, I had fantasised as a child about her moon-lit trek to the Clee Hills in Shropshire, knocking on the workhouse door and all. The truth is she was by then already in her late thirties, working in service at a nearby village, when the deed was done. The child of this unfortunate union was my grandfather who would later marry the daughter of Walter Mann, upon whom the central character of this book is based. In all probability, the father would have been her employer or some other member of the household. It was far from unusual for working women to be abused so by their more-godly overseers. Anyway, that was the tale that started me off researching Walter's life and times and, as a result, writing this book about him, his family, culture, class and, as I quickly came to realise, me.

Before I take my author's sideways step and crack on with this historical tale, I hope you will indulge me, dear reader, with a brief statement of ambition and approach. In academic parlance, my stance is that a social action theory alternative to the miseries and legion limitations of functionalism, in understanding society and what people do within it, has acquired an unhealthy ascendancy. As every sixth-form sociologist will tell you, this means that I reject the view of society as a balancing act between various interests of evenly-matched power: rather, I see it as a bloody battlefield on which one group has an overwhelming arsenal. In other words, we have, at least in the UK, reverted to a 'Whig and Tory' mentality, squeezing out the wisdom and opportunity of conflict theories – marxist, feminist and black perspectives are the standard ones to my mind but there are also shoots of a growing ethic of care for other species, as they struggle to cope with human greed and selfishness. What I am saying (bear with me!) is that a functionalist view of society – one that stresses conformity and subservience to the prevailing socio-economic order – has to be challenged, and challenged hard, in order to produce social justice. The problem with social action approaches is that they're not really up to the task, leaving the way open for the imaging of society as a machine or organism – automobile or amoeba - to prevail. I could argue in a similar vein about 'postmodernism' but would say little as yet unsaid and, no doubt, bore the pants off you. The sharp point to be made though is that, again, there is little left to oppose the relentless march of capitalism. If I may take further leeway, I believe that this ideological closure takes us all out across some very thin ice and it also means that, for many poor buggers, the winter will continue to last a lifetime. So, on that sombre note, I will now take my seat off-stage and wish you a stimulating and challenging read!

It's late July in the year of 1867 at the Shropshire hamlet of New England, part of Highley, a largish village on the western bank of the River Severn and seven miles from Bridgnorth. In a row of roughly-hewn stone cottages, a new-born Walter loudly announces his arrival. It's a Saturday and Caroline, an experienced giver of birth, is already thinking about tomorrow. The parochial charities give £10 a year which is used to buy bread, no fish, for distribution to the poor on Sundays. She might struggle to stand for very long in the queue, paining with torn perineum, and was not convinced that anyone acting in her stead would be recognised as sufficiently worthy. Coming home empty-handed was not an option so Caroline summons her husband,

"John, can you fetch our Sarah from next door, someone needs to get a loaf tomorrow and if she's not there prompt we'll have nothing..."

"Let me worry about that, missus, you've a young 'un just born to feed, I shall call her' shortly.."

"But will you tell 'er to get to the front...you needs to tell her, John, or we shall be without."

"Yes, I shall...I shall tell her."

"Promise me you will?"

"I promises, I promises...now cut yer cackle and put your mind to the little 'un, no doubt he'll want his feed...and by the look of 'im he's going to eat us out of house 'n home...I shall tell her....all in good time."

John Mann softly closes the door and makes his way carefully downstairs. His daughter, Sarah, is already in the kitchen peeling potatoes. Having heard the creaks, she turns from the bowl, deliberately, and catches John with one of them looks that tells you to stop fussing,

"I 'eard, father, I 'eard, and I shall be there even though it hurts me to beg for stale mouldy crust with all the old 'uns, cripples and the Matthews 'uman who is not quite all there..so shut yer yap, I 'eard 'n let us get on with the spuds or you'll be getting no dinner, for what it's worth."

Recognising that Sarah means business, John does what is asked of him and steals out through the back door seeking respite in the garden. He takes off his waistcoat, rolls up his sleeves and opens the shed door to pick out the hoe, always plenty of weeding to be done this time of year. He has put a brave face on inside but is now able to let off steam, jabbing at the ground, a salty tear locked hidden behind his eye.

At this time, William Durham is lord of the manor, seemingly unconcerned by the Mann family's sorry plight. Although William has ready access to money, education, healthcare, in addition to an abundance of food, he chooses not to do anything. Scraps from his breakfast table would amply feed a poor family. Proper cleansing and, perhaps, a stitch or two would help Caroline's sore tear to her perineum heal up quickly without infection - the local quack demanding two shillings before he would even consider administering such simple treatment. The nearest infirmary/ workhouse is at Kidderminster, some sixteen miles away, and no-one goes there unless they are really desperate. They rarely return home.

Walter's father John was born in 1813, apprenticed to and subsequently worked as a stonemason. Later, as his eye-sight began to fail, as a stone cutter's labourer. He worked mainly on churches but Kidderminster was starting to grow and new buildings for commerce and local government were being built. By the time Walter was born in the summer of 1867, John was already a candidate for the knacker's yard and, by then, not the happiest soul in New England. In fact, he was a miserable old bear with a poorly paw at times, although few could blame him given the terrible arthritis that pained his every movement. An outdoor labouring man's hands become deeply-etched by winter cold, repeated trauma and injury. As a child I recall my maternal step-grandfather's fingers, like grotesquely swollen sausages, rough and raw.

Caroline Mann, Walter's mother, was born the third of four children at Highley in 1836. Her mother Ann Middleton worked as a domestic servant and her father Thomas died when she was still an infant. The official cause of death was consumption but his fellow miners believed it was from burning the coal, drift-mined from the Brock Hall Coal Seam worked at Stanley Colliery which closed in 1826. The coal was of poor quality, full of yellow and brown sulphur and used for heating working class cottages and brick making. Thomas, however, had heard from Jack Sodington from the nearby Worcestershire mining village of Mamble that the coal was also good for preserving hops, because of the sulphur, and had tried it out for himself. Draping the hops like a tent over the brick-lined garden fire produced a suffocating array of toxic gases that probably did for him. As important, no doubt, is the fact that many local people suffered ill-health because of the sulphurous fumes, blown back down chimneys or inhaled outdoors on foggy winter days and nights. If you should visit Highley today, you will readily discover a street of sandstone cottages, originally built to house quarrymen's families, evocatively named 'Smoke Alley'. Needless to say, a better class of coal was reserved for those who could pay the extra and afford to live away from these densely-packed homes.

Caroline was a robust young woman who, even dressed in her hand-me-down garb, cut an impressive figure. She had first met John at the Ship Inn where she worked part-time as a general skivvy. She had to help in the house and sometimes carried sacks of coal on her back down to the river as was the custom for Highley women at that time. John was more than twenty years older, could have been her father but she loved him for his kindness and strength. He worked hard in the local sandstone quarry using his long experience as a mason to cut and dress the stone so neat and expertly. Caroline would kiss his cut fingers as she laid alongside him on wintry nights. Small moments of delight in a world of toil and suffering. A world run by rich people who took more than they should. And if you think that's going a bit too far, just picture Caroline as she struggles with that heavy bag of coal down steep, slippery track-ways. Imagine her beginning to feel her age, knowing that she must continue to struggle against hardship and deprivation for years to come, knowing that the most likely outcome for her of a long life of toil would be the abject misery of the workhouse.

Because of the greed and lack of humanity on the part of the powerful, the poor had to fight simply in order to survive.

Walter was thus born into a world of struggle and disquiet in which working people were offered no protection as they battled for their rights. There was violence, inevitably, as night follows day. In Sheffield, iron workers sabotaged the machinery of men who would not join the union and a workman's house was blown up. The Boilermakers' Society took court action against one of its own officials who had stolen funds but the judge said that unions could not sue anyone because there was nothing in law to say they had a right to exist, or to own property, so nothing could be stolen from them. In other words, the fight was dirty and uphill all the way, made so by people who drafted laws solely to serve their own interests. To be fair, not that much has changed once you scratch the surface. Listen to the current batch of Tories and you will know what I mean.

This is not to deny the strides already made by organised labour and other people with a conscience and even by the Tory and Whig governments, as they bribed and sweetened in their desperate attempts to hold back the tide of collectivism and democracy sweeping through nineteenth century Europe. However, many of the changes were simply too distant to be felt in the lives of ordinary people. The 1832 Reform Act, for example, marked an important shift in the balance of power between landed gentry and the middle classes. This affected towns close to Highley, such as Kidderminster, which was made a new borough with one MP, and Wolverhampton, a new borough with two MPs. For the vast majority of working people, including the Mann family, there was little change on the ground because the vote was restricted to men living in houses worth £10 in annual rent. John Mann was thus denied any say in governance while franchise for women like Caroline was even farther away.

As a rule, working conditions remained awful as many

employers simply refused to give a job to anyone unless they signed a pledge that they would not join a trade society or union and the 1830s ended without any trade union left standing, although there were still some trade societies in operation, like the stonemasons' which, of course, became today's freemasons' society. These were dramatic times in the battle for power. After a farcical trial, the Tolpuddle martyrs were transported to Australia in 1834. A strike against wage cuts flared up in the North and Midlands in 1842 under the new Tory government, headed by Sir Robert Peel. The Amalgamated Society of Engineers (ASE), the first really strong trade union was formed in 1851. It was led by William Allan who had a background in the Scottish cotton industry where he had worked his way up from the shop-floor. The Midland Railway Company had just opened its engine works at Crewe and William joined the Journeyman Steam-engine and Machine-makers' Society there, becoming its general secretary in 1848, before encouraging other engineering societies to form the ASE. Again, such developments, at least in the short term, hardly touched the lives of poorer people like the Mann family. Engineers, after all, were relatively well-off and so was their union. On the other hand, William Allan robustly defended the right to join a union and gave generous financial support to building workers while they were out on strike.

Today, New England is a quiet backwater but, in earlier times, it was a very different kettle of fish. There were coal mines, stone quarries and a blast furnace, with a tram shuttling goods back and forth to boats waiting on the River Severn at Highley village nearby. The cottages had been started at the end of the eighteenth century, built by the owners of Billingsley colliery to house their miners (It may surprise readers to know that coal mining on and around the Clee Hills is, in fact, well-documented since the sixteenth century). The pit closed in 1812 and, soon after, the population of the area began to drop. There was little cause to stay at New England and many of the cottages stood empty and rotted in the cold and damp. By the time Walter arrived, the place was little more than a sad and seedy hovel. The toilet, of sorts, was at the end of the row: the water supply a spring on the other side of the pathway. John and Caroline had little option but to stay, on account of his advancing years and poor health. Thankfully, in 1870, coal mining started again at Billingsley and Walter's older brothers found work there, followed by Frank shortly after, while Sarah Mann, Walter's sister, was obliged to stay at home to help look after John. Billingsley was only twenty minutes or so to walk but, with the opening of Highley colliery a few years later, the family was exceptionally well-positioned at New England for employment. Industry meant that people flooded into the area and the cottages were repaired and soon fully occupied, then bursting at the seams. Eventually, the land opposite was used for a sewage works and the cottages condemned towards the end of the First World War. For the moment, though, let's re-join Walter and his family at the beginning of the 1870s.

CHAPTER TWO

School-days, Leaving Home and Hard Graft

Walter's childhood is short-lived and, overall, unpleasant. His family is dirt poor, work hard and grinding, and accommodation dire. Walter, now aged four, has an older sister, Sarah, at home, while his brother Frank is already employed as a quarry labourer, at the tender age of eleven! There are two older brothers, Charles and Edward, although Charles was by then living away from home, in lodgings at Billingsley and working down the pit. Ten years later, Caroline had been widowed, Sarah still at home helping to look after three young siblings. Charles Mann had moved back with the family while Walter had already left home, lodging at 'Smoke Alley' in Highley village and working underground at the colliery.

But first let us step back a few years to Walter's schooldays. Highley Primary School was built in 1861, a few years before the 1870 Board Act. John Davies was the Headmaster, Miss Jessie Thatcher, the assistant teacher, and Mrs Amelia Davies (John's wife) a third teacher. There had been an earlier school, 'The Dame School', run by Miss Doughty from her home at School House, New Road, Highley. The charge of one penny a day was prohibitive for miners' pockets. In other words, it was for posh kids only. The Primary School brought more social mixing although the rich were able to provide home tuition so most of the children at Walter's school were like him, poor. Children from the Workhouse were expected to 'mix in' at the school as well. A young boy called 'Brown' has turned up and is being paraded at the front of Walter's class. The backcloth to this brief drama is a giant map of the world, variously coloured, showing the colonies as red but stained dark blue where an inkwell had been thrown at one of the teachers by a wayward lad days before he went to work in the quarries..

"Now, where shall we ask young Brown to sit?" asks Mrs Davies.

The class shuffles uncomfortably. No-one wants to sit next to the 'workus' boy because he stinks of cabbage and worse but Walter sees Brown drop his eyes and pinch his own arm hard, stifling the emotional pain he is feeling. Walter's heart goes out to him,

"I will Mrs Davies, I will, Brown can sit here next to me", says Walter, ignoring the hand-hidden giggles and open sneers of some of his peers.

"He can sit by me."

At which, Brown was across the front and down the aisle to Watty's row like a lightning-fast greyhound called Speedy, while Walter tried not to flinch, smelling the institutionalised stench sharpened by a more individual whiff of urine from stale trousers. It was never the boy's fault although this is what every day taught him. A dirty little boy, fit for factory at best, perhaps a brief part in an empire-building war, maybe a dose of some nasty disease or disorder based on malnutrition, the possibilities were limited and all distinctly unpleasant for a workhouse child.

As the weeks passed, Walter got to be very fond of Brown, who never developed a first name, and asked his mother if the boy could come home to live. Walter knew what the workhouse was like. He had visited there to sing Christmas carols for the older residents. There was the cabbage stink and lots of dark green paint everywhere to reinforce the smell of it. The men broke stone or chopped up railway sleepers for firewood, to sell round the posh houses. The women sewed for their sins. There was no way that Brown or any other child should have to stay there, so Walter had it all worked out, how he would share his food and Brown could sleep in his and Frank's bed. It would be a bit crowded but that could be gotten used to. Of course, from Caroline Mann's perspective, such a thing was a non-starter given the limited rations and space available. There was simply no chance of it happening and, having been told for the umpteenth time, Walter eventually cried himself to sleep thinking about Brown's sorry lot. He was overcome by sadness but strong in his care for others, a strength that would feed his anger in later years.

On a brighter note, there were some advantages to living at Highley, surrounded by countryside, animals domesticated and wild, and the mighty Severn running close by. Every child would be firmly instructed to keep away from the river but few would be able to resist its temptations. A number of young lives were claimed and some not so young too were taken down to the dark pools that lay beneath the river's swirls and strong currents. New England was safer, though not so thrilling. The damson tree was a favourite of the children, climbing and shaking it and, in season, tasting the sharp, purple-skinned fruit. Wasps battled for their autumnal share while fast-flying red admiral butterflies sought anything over-ripe, resting in the highest branches before swooping down to plunder the soft delights. On Sundays, Walter might spend time held in the branches, thinking about what his father John had told him, about how big 'Kiddie' (Kidderminster) was and how high the church was, and Walter could picture himself climbing the ladders and chipping the stone into wondrous gargoyles and angels. Then he would be sinking into the black mud at the tree's base, ice-cold water easily entering Frank's clodhopper, hand-me-down boots to end his reverie.

"Watty's got a bootie, Watty's got a bootie...wetty, wetty Watty" and similar astute observations made by his fellows soon brought Walter fully returned to the real world.

As he squelched towards the stone wall where he might remove his wet things, Walter looked skywards and saw a crow taking on a sparrow hawk. The crow was fearless and would not relent even though the hawk could despatch it readily. But Walter was more impressed by the hawk. It reminded him of how he felt when plagued by the little 'uns. Even as a young boy, he felt different, a falcon amongst finches, an eagle set apart. This was his fantasy, something that would sustain and betray him for all but the last few years of his life.

Then off, running hard back to the cottage, for tea which consisted of one slice of bread and home-made jam, last year's damson of course, a thin slice of cake and a mug of lukewarm 'rosie lea' or skimmed milk, if he was lucky. Not a great deal for a growing boy but no more could be had because there was no more. No second slice of bread. No fatter slice of cake. Nothing. Every night Walter went to bed hungry, dreaming of food. Shame on those who had plenty and did nothing to ease the suffering of poor children. Today the damson tree has many offspring, more of a thicket really but, if you look hard enough, you can just see the foundations of a row of stone cottages, all that is left of Walter's home and childhood playground. If you listen, you can still hear the laughter alongside the bubbling water and chilling wind. There is also a more disturbing sound for those who can bear to listen.

John Mann died when he was sixty-five, no great span by today's expectations but a good age during that period in history. He had worked hard until the arthritis got hold of him, turning his fingers round on themselves and his hands to useless claws. He died in his sleep and Walter was encouraged to say bye-bye to his dad laid out in the front parlour. John had been shaved posthumously for the final time and there was a trace of blood on his neck that caught the boy's attention. Kept him from looking at his dad's closed eyes, already shrinking small in their sockets. At such a tender age, this was a tough thing to do but Walter bravely touched his father's face before grabbing his mum's arm and the tears came like a torrent.

Highley Colliery really got going in 1878 and was soon acting like a magnet to all the youngsters from the village and surrounding area. Walter was aged eleven by then and had already worked for a year or so at the quarry, fetching, carrying and taking cider and sharpened tools to the men as they cut the sandstone. The prospect of coal-mining was exciting, it paid more money and so Walter was off, although the skills he had picked up would serve him well later cutting the much harder dhustone. Young spirits innocent of their prospects, ready like standing corn for the sharp edge of unfettered capitalism.

Walter's first taste of working at the colliery was not to his liking. He spent long hours operating the pump that shifted water from the narrow tunnels before being allowed to help drag the cut coal away from the face back to the wooden trams or 'wagons' pulled by ponies up to the shaft. He was a strong boy for his age, fearless of the enclosed, dank conditions and was quickly promoted to 'miner',

"Yer han's pouring blood again Walter...these fuckin' 'oles are not driven big enough for rats", says one of the pony men in the half-light of a candle.

"If I hit 'em once more on the sides this morning I shall quit it 'n go back to the quarrying..."

"You have to get used to it, lad, whoever it was that made the tunnels never thought about your health nor comfort, that's a fact. Take a look at my hands. See, the knuckles are still swollen even after years out of the tunnels minding this old nag."

"They should try it themselves, just for an hour or so, then they'd think different, this is a hell-hole and a bloody slog", Walter says as he prepares to push his tram back up to the boy ahead working from the coal-face, in even tighter conditions.

Toiling hard and long underground helps build strong bonds and a sure sign of this were the nicknames workers used for each other. Even if you had already been rechristened, like Walter who was widely known as 'Watty' (as in 'Ratty'), your workmates felt duty-bound to do the honours. So, Walter was named 'Ginger Biscuit' on account of his hair colour and complexion. This was frequently foreshortened to 'Biscuit' after a day or two of the fuller title. His best mate John Raine was inevitably 'Joyful' given his surname and accompanying temperament of woe. Then there was Frank, Walter's older brother, known as 'Cider' and skinny Thomas Upham affectionately, though not especially imaginatively, as 'Whippet'.

Of course, the strength of these bonds spilled over into the little break time available to workers. Picture, if you will, the group eating their 'bait' underground at the base of the pit-shaft. Watty, aged seventeen years and a few months, is now a young man with stubble on his chin and some suggestion of a moustache. Cider Frank is off his food due to a surfeit of scrumpy the previous night so is sharing his box out amongst the others,

"I swear it was off, Biscuit, it tasted like sugared piss water...an' as cloudy as milk, them Trimbles are known for throwing rats in it...now, have another one a Mary's rock cakes won't ya?"

"Am at Stokes' bridge already Frank, I cunna eat no more, says Walter, also feeling the effects."

"Cummon, you're the gutsiest bugger I ever knew. It has been told by people who was there at the same table and at the same time that you bust your in-laws' to be best dinner plate, getting the gravy up with your knife," Cider now teasing and playing it up to the gallery,

"But, I never did such a daft trick, it was a cracked plate they give me," replies the Biscuit, "only half-convincingly as he realised his admission half way through the sentence. It was not the thing to do in polite company, irrespective of the crockery's poor state of repair.

"Getting the gravy up is what I 'eard. And from them who deserve to be believed. They says you busted it and then there was such a look of shocked amazement on the faces of your prospective family, and even the lodger was truly amazed, you never went there again…and that's despite being sweet on the daughter."

"Don't believe all you're told, ya droopy-arsed wassock."

"Getting up the gravy it was....and they says you bent the knife an' all...Besides, I've seen you eat a whole rabbit, out near the Mount it was, if you remembers dear old Watty boy, just by Kinlet Hall, and that's without even skinning nor paunching him," chirps in the Whippet with a cheeky grin all across his cheery chops.

"And you're a mischievous and cocksure young semblance of a fella, Whippet. You knows I anna done rabbitin' down Kinlet way for years, on account of the run-in me and John had with the master, as he calls himself…." with which Walter means to finish the crack and the men lift themselves wearily for another go at the seam. It's the precise moment that Joyful pipes in,

"What was that all about then Watty? I never 'eard what 'appened between your old man and the master, old Bluntie...what was it that did take place?

"Not somethin' I likes to jaw about, Joyful, but I'll tell ya if it'll get ya back to work....What 'appened was John caught the old man Blunt, britches down and ass in the air staring skywards round back of St Peter's...we was taking a shortcut through the churchyard, making our way to Windwoods to help dig Martha Jackson's garden for her...anyway, he was on the job with one of the Pritchards, barely thirteen years, not much older than myself at the time...none too pleased neither when he caught sight of us with shock and smiles of some proportion breaking out across our faces...not at all pleased, you would have to say, I dunna know if he was at the sour-strokes point in the exercise and stoppin' was not then his first consideration."

"So, what did 'e do, Biscuit, did 'e try to restrain himself at all, surely 'e did that?"

"It was too late, Joyful, so he was obliged to maintain matters until full completion took place....it was only a while later that he caught up with John 'n me 'n tore us off a strip...said we should never tell a living soul, and told us both to keep away from the village on pain of something nasty...John would have smacked him, I believe, if I hadn't pulled him away..."

"Dirty bastards, the lot of 'em," says Frank, "and our Sarah's hoping to start at the big house after Easter...if he so much as lays a finger on her, I shall hang him up by his dick...I shall swing for 'im, I swear."

"You'll be some way back in the queue Cider, I shall want first go and I promises there won't be much left of the sod for afters. Anywards, to finish the tale, ...ever since, I've been keeping clear of Kinlet and roundabout there, as I've an idea I'd get a sight more than the lock-up from old master Blunt, should he lay his mitts upon me."

"But why was he so put out, Watty, his lot 'as been shaggin' our young girls since as long as anyone can recall?"

"It wasna a girl, Joyful, it was young Sam Pritchard, Martha the widow's boy, the one who's missin' a slate or two, he's such a simple lad, he wouldna entirely know what was taking place…I reckon that was what shamed the bugger so."

At this there is astonishment cracked by a shared laugh, turning to varied showings of disgust, finally to resigned contempt before they rise up, as one, ready for work. Martha was poorest of the poor, a widow with young mouths to feed. She'd begged for help but got herself in debt and the bum bailiffs, named such because of their proximity to people's behinds as they chased up what was owed, had been round,

"Now Martha, why would you want four chairs? With your husband long gone, lying in the churchyard. What use has he of it?"

"Have you no heart at all", she replies, "he's not yet cold in his grave, a pauper's grave at that, is there nothing sacred to you both? The little 'uns still calls it father's chair' and they puts his old boots in front of it."

"Four chairs. Four chairs, that's what's 'ere, I can count 'em. And you only need three, so you must sell one to pay your debts. That is what you must do, Mrs Jackson, otherwise we shall be calling again to take it, make no mistake, or maybe we shall be taking 'em all, be warned now, be warned by what I've told you."

Watty had heard of the widow's plight and visited to offer whatever assistance he could give. Rough digging the back garden was what was needed and Watty took only a few hours to oblige. When he heard the story about the four chairs he asked Martha if she would like the bailiff to meet some unfortunate mishap, perhaps on his way home from the pub one moon-free night. Watty knew where the man sank his ale and had quickly worked out the best way to dust him up convincingly in the darkness. Martha though was wiser than that so declined the offer. She knew it might only make matters far worse for her and hers. Watty too if they ever found out who'd done the deed. He was only a youngster after all and, despite his size, he needed protecting. She would say nothing. 'Grin and bear it' is what poor people soon learn to do.

The men nearly always frequented the same pub, the Royal Oak, of a Saturday evening. Just occasionally they might make their way across to the Dhustone Inn, especially on a warm summer evening. Apart from chapel, this was about all there was outside work because everyone had to tend their vegetable garden and do other jobs in order to make ends meet. In addition to raising cabbages, spuds, onions and beans on his patch, Walter helped keep the graveyard tidy, for sixpence every two weeks. Frank, for his part, helped out Jenkins the undertaker when called upon. Rabbiting was a popular night-time occupation for some but it would have been foolhardy to talk openly about it, given the gamekeeper's long ears, and so the best banter was restricted to the back room, where all could be trusted. And good banter it was too,

"What you smokin' in that fuckin' pipe? asks Watty of his older cousin Jack Preece.

"That's coltsfutt, Watty my boy, collected it myself off the top and dried 'n mixed it to a special recipe that I could share with ya for a small sum," replies Jack.

"I've no call for it, Jack, apart from it stinks like the devil, I cunna be doing with such mucky habits."

"He's got far worse habits than smoking shit," pipes in Jack's brother Freddy.

"Now you must tell me about 'em in every detail," answers Watty, working on Jack's growing annoyance and fighting back his own amusement.

"Just ask to see the palm of his right hand, Watty, and you'll be amazed at the hairiness of it, just ask him to show it now if you've a will."

At this, Jack's patience is exhausted and he is up and chasing Freddy round the room while Watty laughs loud at the two young goon-fowls. But away home to his bed he must go, having a long and arduous trek to endure the following morning.

It was still unusual for working people to travel far in the late 19th century unless they were moving in search of work but this was not the reason for Walter journeying to Hereford. Instead, he was off by invite to visit his uncle who had worked in the nearby limestone quarries. Again, this was a rare sort of event given the demands of work and family but Watty wanted to see his relative one last time. After years of inhaling the dust, Jim was now coughing blood and very close to the end, for which he was grateful it must be said. After a long journey on foot, down country in late autumn, Watty caught sight of the red sandstone cathedral spire and knew he was near to Hereford. He had drunk from streams, eaten blackberries and hazel nuts, stolen an apple or two and even found a hen's egg, eaten raw, to satisfy his hunger. Dusty and tired, turning by the Market Tavern, he reaches his destination and knocks on the door which opens to reveal a worn-looking woman of forty years,

"You're a sight for the sorest eyes, Walter Mann" says Jim's wife Margaret. "Jim'll be tickled you've come…come in and make yourself at home. Have you eaten? I've some bread and rabbit stew if you'd care for some. Sit yourself down, here at the table and I'll fetch you a plateful."

"Thank you kindly, Maggie, I'm dusty from the road…"

"Don't be daft. You've no need to be worried at all about that…would you like to wash first? I can fill a bowl from the kettle, the water's piping…My and how you've grown tall since I last saw ya. You're full-grown and…what's that under your nose? Is it a mushroom? "

Watty blushes and swiftly makes his way to the wash-bowl as Margaret continues to make a fuss of him. He splashes his face in the water, washes his hands thoroughly and dries himself on the warm towel given to him. This is wonderful comfort after his journey. After a warm helping of food, Watty is shown up the steep stairs to the bedroom. Jim lies there, propped up with pillows, a bedspread wrapping his shoulders,

"Watty, come sit…come sit here by me….it's a joy to see ya again, how have you been? Has mother fed you?" Jim is struggling hard for breath but determined to make every use of Watty's visit.

"I've bin well looked after, Jim. I'm washed and fed. Can I get ya anything before I sits down?"

"I'm in need of nothing, Watty, now's you're here….tell me about Carrie and the boys. Are you still at Highley pit ? The size of you….you must be cutting the coal by now?"

"Still there, Jim…although my heart's not in it, being underground is not my most favoured place. I'm at the face now, as you says, but then it won't be too long before I'm back at the quarry…at least a man can look up there at the sky and breath fresh air while he's working."

"That's the truth, Watty, you're thinking straight there. Get out while you can, lad. Take a look at me and recall how fit I was when you and John used to come to help with digging the garden. My lungs is nine parts stone dust. I'm a dying man, Watty, I shan't see ya again, I knows that."

Jim puts his hand shakily on Walter's wrist and leans towards him,

"Listen, I shan't see ya again but I'm very glad you've come to see me and I wants ya to stay as long as you can, it's no trouble to Maggie....but I'm tired now and will have to rest".

Watty straightens the bedding where he's been sitting and tip toes to the door, taking what turns out to be his last look at Jim before he dies.

The going rate for a bed (shared with someone and, often, something else) at this time in history was three old pennies a night in the Manchester slums. In Hereford it was both cheaper and less costly in blood lost to bed bugs and fleas but Watty would not be allowed to even mention payment anyway. He was with his own family and class. He would be fed well, simple fare but filling and nutritious. Across the water, whole swathes of the population would do much worse. The Irish Famine had hit hard again in January 1880. Typhus followed hard on its heels, bringing disaster and misery to poor communities. At the beginning of March, the farmers were obliged to hire labourers again but, in the meantime, the peasants had starved and shivered to death. Karl Marx died on the 14th March three years later. He had founded the International so that workers might pool their rights and energies thereby stopping capitalists dividing them up by 'nation' and playing them off against each other. At the time, his death went widely unacknowledged and, of course, the flagrant disregard for the working classes by the powerful continued. Jim lasted only a few days but he was made up to have seen Watty one last time. No doctor could have saved him, both lungs were shot from the limestone dust, but the pain could have been alleviated had the family enough money to pay for morphine which, since the invention of the hypodermic needle in 1853, had become the standard treatment in such circumstances (the more powerful invoker of dreams, heroin did not reach the marketplace until 1898). Had his employers given a damn, Jim might have been spared or, at very least, comforted in his agony. Watty was, of course, unaware of the link between such individual miseries and Marx's ideas and, as a young uneducated man, his concerns were understandably elsewhere, at least for the time being.

CHAPTER THREE

Breweries, Tanneries and Courting

It was in Hereford, during this short visit to see his uncle, that Watty, now aged eighteen, had the greatest fortune to meet his darling Mary. To introduce her, this is Mary Ann Harmison, daughter of Patrick and Catherine. Ellen is her younger sister, James and Edward her younger brothers. Mary had already been working at the Hereford and Tredegar Brewery for many years. Catherine, a lively southern Irish woman, works there too while Patrick is employed at the nearby tannery. All four children were born in the little village of Ocle Pychard in Herefordshire. Their parents, originally from County Cork, began their time in England as 'estate workers', apple picking and hop work by season, and the family, like the Manns, lived at the evocatively and tellingly named 'Sheds'. They were so-called because of their makeshift nature, corrugated iron rooves and, as can readily be imagined, they were far from pleasant to live in. Not warm, not even rain-proof nor, in any way, inspiring. No roses round the door. In fact, the Harmisons' accommodation was appalling. Just as Frederick Engels had found in Manchester, these hard-working people were obliged to suffer the deprivations and degradations of slum-life. Slums set in the countryside but slums all the same. In stark contrast, still stands the local manor house, set with mighty conifers and resplendent in its red Hereford sandstone. Of course, for Patrick and Catherine, pretty much anything was an improvement on their life in Ireland. Patrick had been just seventeen when the potato blight first arrived, carried across the Atlantic from Mexico via the USA. After a series of failed harvests, accompanied by outbreaks of cholera and typhus, perhaps two thirds of the population had been killed or left. A minority who rebelled against their English overlords were transported or otherwise harshly dealt with. The Hamison family were pitched out of their home, lock, stock and barrel. Patrick's younger brother had Down's Syndrome and died from pneumonia in the workhouse. His grandmother finished her days in a similar fashion. Central government aid in the shape of the Soup Kitchens Act was ended in September 1847 and local poor rates and charities were expected to shoulder an impossible weight of demand. The rural areas of County Cork were very badly hit. In amongst this mayhem and misery, Patrick courted Catherine, his childhood sweetheart, and the pair were married before joining the tide of emigrants northwards then across the water to Liverpool. They made their way slowly southward, finding odd days of casual work where they could before 'settling' in Herefordshire.

Patrick was glad of the regular work at the tannery in Barton Road but hated what he had to do every day. The work was hard but the stench was more acrid than any person should reasonably be expected to bear. There was a little compensation in knowing that the smell was not as bad as it once was – in medieval times, animal brains, dog shit and human piss were used on the skins, with the tanner using his bare feet to work the chemistry. It was still bad enough though and Patrick coughed his lungs and heart out each day after work. His job was to 'scud' the hides with a blunt scraper after the machine had removed what it could of the animal hair. Cold foggy mornings were worst, with no breeze and the high water vapour content rending the air virtually unusable. For some peculiar reason, Patrick had a soft spot for the royalty, particularly the queen and even for her lover prince Albert who had been dead since 1861, possibly even before for all intents and purposes, while Catherine nurtured a deep anger for the lot of them. Angry that rich people with responsibility could let others, children, the old and the sick suffer. Angry that they chose not to use their power to lighten the burden on the backs of the poor. Angry at the sickening displays of pomp and circumstance while her children Mary, Ellen, James and Edward had next to nothing. Being Irish, she had little fondness for Oliver Cromwell but, nevertheless, thought of the English Civil War as a missed opportunity. A chance to have gotten rid of the greedy rotten parasites for good, as she might say,

"They're worse than no use, Pat, they're a deadly harm for us poor folk."

"How can you say such things, my lovely? Take the queen, if you will...now there is a woman of such dignity, of such noble birth and bearing, she holds up a golden framed mirror to the country and asks us to follow in her greatness..."

"I suspect the tannery is addling your brain, what little you started with. Even I should be great, dignified and noble with a tenth of her vast income and investment. She drips with jewels and is as fat as a late autumn pig..."

"So now tell me what you would do with our royals, Cath? In your wondrous scheme of things, what would befall them?"

"Those that would work for a living should be spared. Those who chose to continue their wicked arrogance would be taught a lesson," she replied, without any pause for thought.

"And what of them who might oppose the changes to their fortune you so zealously promote, dear heart?"

"I know where you are heading me with such questions, Pat. We have travelled this old road together many times. Nevertheless, I shall answer you direct. There might be call for some measure of violence against those who refuse to change their ways and, I have no doubt, some who would prefer to have their necks stretched rather than bend."

"That amounts to murder…."

"Do you believe that the high and mighty are not themselves guilty of murder, as we speak, every single day of their lives? "

"It occurs to me that some might be even higher than before, what with their longer necks and all…"

"You always makes a joke, Pat, but this is no laughing matter for me."

"The trouble with you Catherine Harmison is you have no sense of the wonderful history of this country," says Pat, looking for a way of gentling the conversation and succeeding.

Catherine's fierce hatred of royalty was fed by a number of fires but the important point is that her heart-felt animosity passed on via Mary Ann to Walter. She was a deeply religious person, raised as a catholic, in a catholic family and community but she had also chosen to stay a catholic and this was the important part of it for her. Catherine saw no contradiction between her faith and her opinions about royalty; for her the church was there to protect the poor. Walter gained much from this thinking and was able to move beyond it to see the role that religion played in maintaining capitalism and all its various trappings.

Like her mother, Mary was a brewery worker. She had started at the age of eleven after years of casual employment on farms and then at a local inn. She was glad of the steady wage, albeit a pittance, and got used to the range of stinks from the brewing process. Mary made full use of her time and learned every facet of beer-brewing. Later on, she would become a brewer of ales and ciders, and famous for her prowess right across the Clee Hills. She was a fine looking young woman too and, initially, the butt of unwanted sexualised insult from her male brewery colleagues. 'Initially' because her temper, once displayed, kept all but the most foolhardy at bay. She could punch her weight and few men would risk their reputation, at least in public. When she first saw Walter though, Mary knew he was a very different and better prospect - strong but not arrogant about it - and that she would want him for herself.

Time was short as it always is for people with only their labour to sell and Watty needed to get back to Highley and his hard work underground. He and Mary had visited the Market Tavern, she the snug and he the public bar but their eyes had met fleetingly, but enough, through the adjoining passageway. Mary was brimmed with confidence and a glass or three so she walked round to him and, with only a hint of hesitation in her voice, started their first conversation. Walter was a little taken aback but glad of such a pretty face and lively temperament. He walked her home, by circuitous route including a stretch of the Wye's riverbank, while she promised to visit in two weeks time. Mary had relatives to stay with at Caynham and was confident that she could find work at one of the local public houses, many brewing their own beer and potential beneficiaries of her considerable expertise.

After a brief spell with her uncle and aunt, Mary took lodgings, still in the village, at the Cleetons' house which, although much smaller and noisy with a seeming inexhaustible multitude of children, better suited her lively temperament. She quickly found work as a domestic servant, on a temporary basis, at the vicarage and was able to save a few shillings from her employment. This was supplemented by a little money earned through the sale of bottles of home-made rhubarb wine, 'rhubarb whiskey' as it was called. The combined sum, Mary put towards her 'bottom drawer'. She soon became very fond of Mrs Annie Cleeton, who always appeared to be doing at least a dozen different things at once, all with no little aplomb, and, when the time came, was very sad to take her leave. Caynham was used as a supply centre during the Civil War and, to this day, many of the military workings remain to shape the landscape. A prominent landmark, known as Caynham 'Camp', was used by Oliver Cromwell to marshal his troops before attacking Ludlow. However, this Iron Age hill-fort had been inhabited and sculpted by people way back beyond the seventeenth century. Mary and Annie are out walking upon it, a few days before Mary's wedding,

"I shall miss this dark green country," she says, feasting on the widening view down 'cross Ledwyche Brook as it meanders through the fields and limestone woodland. Clee Hill is a barren place by comparison, wind-swept and devoid of all but the smallest specimens of hawthorn and mountain ash. "And I shall miss you, Annie, my dear, you've been a true friend over these past months…"

"A pleasure, Mary, a pleasure it has been", replies her companion, as the pair walk arm-in-arm up the steep side and then there is Ludlow itself in full perspective, a towering St. Lawrence's Church, wondrous Norman castle and all.

"You will have to come visiting once Watty and me are settled in our own home. We shall have to live with Caroline for a while but that won't be a bad thing as she's a goodly soul and we shall get on fine. Still, it will be a little while before we have our own place but the time will rush by, no doubt, I shall be married and, I hope, we shall be blessed with some little 'uns...then you and I shall swap stories next to the fire and I'll hold back a bottle of elderflower wine, your favourite, which we shall keep to ourselves".

"Now that's a treat I canna pass up, Mary, 'though I'll be surprised if Watty lets you hold even a bottle back, knowing how good you makes it......Anyways my dear, I wishes you every possible happiness...you're a fine catch for your man, who I knows loves you with all his heart, and, though I shan't have time to visit you for some years, what with so much to do, the children and baby on the way, you will be in my thoughts...I shan't forget your hard work, always done with a willingness and kind heart..."

"And I will miss you, Annie, you've been like a sister and a mother to me", Mary utters, with tears falling like rain into the short grass.

Walter and Mary married in the summer of 1886. Not much of a do but neither was particularly concerned with the trappings. The passing of the Married Women's Property Act in 1882 meant that Mary was allowed to keep the gold half-sovereign given to her by her aunt – before the Act, even this modest heirloom would have become Watty's, on their marriage.

As the couple come out from the tiny Norman church into the glorious sunlight, Walter looks up to see the house martins darting against a cloudless sky. Higher up the larger swifts are showing off their seemingly effortless skills. "Not much of a catch for either of 'em", he whispers to himself, starting a smile on his whiskered face. For her part, Mary feels so pleased with her small bunch of wild flowers, selected from the buzzing richness of nature that accompanies the lanes winding up steeply to Titterstone. This was a fine day and Walter would provide well for her. She felt for him, was moved by him and tingled with excitement. What else was there but to be happy and content with her lot?

The warm glow of satisfaction continued well into the autumn. Yes, Watty spent most of his time at work, while Mary helped Caroline with the household duties and worked part-time at the Nag's Head, but there were moments of true affection and closeness between them. Two young lovers, when all is said and done. Sunday afternoon finds the pair out on the high heath-land picking bilberries,

"They calls 'em winberries up Church Stretton way, Mary, so's I'm told", offers Watty.

"Always been wimbrey, as long as I can recall", replies Mary, her finger-ends a deep purple from the dark staining berry juice. "Anyhow, they taste very well and we shall make a giant of a pie with what's in our baskets. I might even use some for dyeing your pants, if you ask me nicely".

"My hands 'ain't made for berry-picking, darling, I've squashed more than I've picked....and you leave my under-garments well-alone or I shall be obliged to take stern measures with you".

"Not the black 'uns, Watty," she says fussing, "them's crowberries...we shall pick them another time...a wimbrey pie is what I'm planning...Look you've got cowberries as well", she taunts him, winging the red intruders accurately, albeit at close range, catching him on the neck with her first throw and leaving a red mark. Watty replies with a salvo of his own but Mary ducks successfully and moves towards him with clear intention.

There's not a soul in sight so Mary takes her man down to lie in the bracken and heather. She carefully ensures there are none of the juicy black or red berries to stain their clothing, while Watty is too full of ardour to concern himself very much about such things. Any adders have already been scared off by the drum of their footsteps. An inquisitive sheep, wool weather-worn and busy chewing, raises itself up to cock an eye before disappearing again within the proud boulders and deep foliage. The couple's physical passion is quick yet mutually fulfilling. Driven by the excitement of being out in the open air, a deep care for each other and the natural springiness of the mattress lying beneath them. They rest for what seems an age, holding and talking silly. As Mary enjoys her forty winks or so, Watty lies there still, enjoying the scents and sights of his surroundings. He notices a small orange butterfly with dark markings on its wings, sitting on worn granite, sheltering from the wind and soaking up the sun. Quietly watching this exquisite insect, Watty's thoughts turn back to his bleak schooldays. He wonders why he was taught nothing about such beautiful creatures. What should he call it? Does it live through the winter? What does it feed on? Many similar questions come to mind before the small copper is gone, dashing after a ragged meadow brown daring to intrude upon its territory. Watty's attention shifts to playfulness as he uses a long grass stem to tickle Mary's face. She awakes with a splutter and scolds him warmly for letting her sleep. When the couple arise it is nearly tea-time. They straighten and tidy each other, then a final embrace before setting off down the steep paths homewards.

"I bin thinking, while you was asleep..."

"Always a worry, Watty, when you've been thinking", quips Mary.

"No, I'm being serious, darlin. I was thinking about why we knows so little of the living things around us. I knows you can name the berries, which comes from you making wines and drinks and such, but there's so much we don't know anything about, nothing...I was watching a tiny insect in the heather, a wonderful little creature it was yet I knows nothing about it."

"And what would you want to know that for?"

"That's it Mary, not 'for' any reason at all, just for its own sake I should like to know."

"You're a rum 'un, Walter Mann, as daft as a duck and as mad as a moorhen!" Mary replies.

"You've a way with words, Mary, but I've never thought of moorhens as mad. But, listen, what I'm wondering is why we was never taught these things while we was at school. I should have liked to have been taught and I wants to know why we wasn't", answers Watty who points his finger skywards and quickens his pace.

There are anvil clouds in the distance, already affecting the light, so the pair make merry haste. Watty notices how dark the ivy wrapped willows look down below, hugging the brook, but he takes special care not to miss his footing. Mary holds his arm tightly.

By the end of November 1886, Mary had miscarried once and conceived her first child. She and Watty were still living with his family in Highley and conditions were cramped, although not unbearably so. Nevertheless, Mary was longing to move into her own home and Watty often had a wasp in his ear from her about this. Caroline Mann was easy enough to get on with but there were Watty's three brothers and two daughters, plus the lodger to consider as well. The prospect of a new baby made moving out both necessary and urgent and the couple would have to take what they could get, although this would have to wait until the New Year, at least.

In the winter months, various methods were devised to alleviate the tedium of work, early nights and poor weather. Playing practical jokes was a favourite pastime and one or two of the men were past masters at it. The best jokes became the stuff of folklore, retold and embroidered to attentive audiences in the gas-lit cottages and public houses. For instance, there was the time when old Bert Brewster fell asleep on his horse and cart. He awoke to find himself and cart on one side of a set of iron railings and the horse, still hitched up to the cart, the other side. Many such tricks were played on the unsuspecting and intoxicated. In addition, men would attempt feats at best unwise, dangerous sometimes and, just occasionally, impossible. Like Ned Armstrong for instance, the blacksmith who, on hands and knees, tested his head-butting prowess against a young goat, a 'tup', and regretted it for more than a month. Ned got down, cider-powered, dropping his head to challenge the goat and he received an almighty crack for his pains. Goats are built for butting while blacksmiths are not, after all is said and done.

For women, such larking about was seen as a luxury. They lived in a world where drudgery rarely even took short pause for breath. Most sang in the chapel on a Sunday. There was also a thin slice of candle- or gas-lit time of an evening when young 'uns were settled in bed. This was used for sewing and darning, alongside the chat with family or near neighbours. Aside from these brief moments, it was all hard slog. Mary recognised this but did not falter at the prospect of it. To a point, it would be fair to say that she would not know what else to do and, no doubt, there is considerable comfort to be drawn from doing what is expected, to 'fit in' with the prevailing patterns of life. On the other hand, the courage of working women should not be disregarded. Carrying on in the face of such desperately tough conditions deserves unqualified recognition.

CHAPTER FOUR

Life at The Sheds

Echoing her father's first shouts at the world some twenty years earlier, Walter and Mary's first-born child, Sarah, announced her arrival in the July of 1887. The couple would have six children in total, including the twins, John and Peter, born in 1891, and 'young Frank', in 1895. The 'Sheds' are a line of sorry, half-timbered hovels, some with turf and others roofed with corrugated iron.

Walter had no schooling after the age of ten and was unable to sign his name up until he was twenty. He was taught to do this by Albert Watson who had lived at the Sheds in Coreley. Albert, for some strange reason known as 'Joe', had been properly educated because his father James was well-to-do, at one time occupying the position of 'agent to the collieries'. Walter had a soft spot for Joe though, in many ways, they were chalk and cheese. Physically Walter was a giant of a man while Joe was slight and walked with a limp, having what the locals called a 'gammy fut'. They shared a love of horses though and, also, love of a pint or two of locally-concocted cider, sweet, cloudy and lethal. Joe was not popular with the rest of his family. He was regarded as a disappointment, not having achieved as well as his older brothers. Some said he was the runt of the litter but what he had was a vision of how things could be different. That was a dangerous possession to have in the 19th century. It was Joe's tuition that helped Walter come to understand his life and conditions in a way that many working people missed or avoided, through fear as much as anything but also because of the brainwashing babble of nation, race, monarchy and religion they suffered. Joe had long experimented with Marx's ideas and could talk about the 'bourgeoisie' and 'proletariat' with the best of them but, in Walter's hands, communism became something very different, something all together more dangerous. He was a powerful man in many ways. Physically, there was none tougher on the Clee Hills and the effect of this was magnified by an iron resolve. A gaggle of burly miners or quarrymen would quieten when he approached. Getting on the wrong side of him was not to be recommended. When moved to action, Walter would eye his opponent in the same, merciless way that an eagle looks at its prey. But, there was much more to him than this. He had a sharp mind, albeit untutored, and, politically, Walter was also no slouch. His mother Catherine's influence was behind this know-how, although it would be many years before that particular penny would drop for Walter. He had worked a lot of it out for himself, the excuses used for not having a trade union and the ways the bosses manipulated and coerced his class. He wanted to change things but knew that he should not advertise his new-found education. He would remain guarded about his beliefs about a new world order. He would avoid the traps set by gaffers, gentry and bible-bashers. For many years, he would continue to sign his name with a cross.

On a wider stage, this was a time when some workers' representatives were beginning to pull away from their traditional association with the Liberal Party. At the TUC conference in 1887, Henry Broadhurst came under vitriolic attack from James Keir Hardie, an ex-miner who became secretary of a Scottish miners' union. Keir Hardie argued that trade unions should back their own working class party independent of the Liberals. Broadhurst had first worked as a stonemason, tramping from town to town in search of work. He ended up in London and eventually became secretary of the Stonemason's Union. In 1875 he had risen to become secretary of the TUC's parliamentary committee and led groups of union leaders to Whitehall and No.10. By the time James took him to task, Henry was already very well-established. But this was also a time when the male-dominated establishment, including 'socialism', was facing sustained questioning from the women's movement. Despite his record of fighting oppression and injustice, Broadhurst was, himself, firmly against women's suffrage. He was described as a 'middle-class philistine' by Beatrice Webb who met him in Dundee, September 1889. That same year, Walter discovered the two authors of communism, Karl Marx and Frederick Engels. He was given a copy of a new English version of the Communist Party Manifesto – the translation was undertaken by Samuel Moore and the small book had been published in 1888. By the time he received it, the book was decidedly worse for wear, dog-eared and dirty, but this mattered not a jot to Watty as he worked his way eagerly through its pages. He had a habit of licking his bounteous moustache when reading or otherwise engaged in deep thought. As he sucked away with such zestful enthusiasm when studying this small but erudite tome from Marx and Engels, it was apparent that they were giving him something substantial to think about. Either that or he had soaked up, and was revisiting, a supply of broth surplus from mealtime.

By the time he was just twenty five, Walter had three of his own children to support. In addition, he had taken three of his nieces under his roof following the tragic death of their parents.

Both had been killed when their cottage caught fire. The three girls had been out on the heath playing when it happened so had, thankfully, been spared the worst. Rose, the eldest, was already doing a few hours cleaning at one of the 'big' houses so was able to contribute something towards her keep. The other two girls were still at school so the burden on the family's finances was considerable. On the other hand, the family was by no means unusually large. Just two doors down, James and Sarah Hopton had ten children, which would have been thirteen if all had survived into infancy. Sarah was just thirty nine years of age. Both she and James suffered rheumatism from the cold and wet. Watty sometimes watched James and saw his own future. At last pig-killing time, when the men would drag the poor doomed animal out from its sty, James had hardly been able to do anything to assist, with so little strength left in him. Mary and Sarah helped each other out with childminding, wash-day and the like, keeping cheerful as much as they were able to and making the best life they could for their respective families, as women do.

The turn of the century was an incredibly important time for working people and their representatives. In the 1892 General Election, our friend Keir Hardie stood in West Ham (south) as an independent candidate, won and was the first working-class MP who refused to support the Liberal Party. There were just three independent Labour members but it was something to cheer, at last, and Watty's heart missed a beat or two when he heard the news. It was high summer and he was busy in the fields when Joe told him. Word had come to Joe via a railway union man called 'Shunter' who worked at Ludlow station. In 1893, Keir Hardie set up the Independent Labour Party but the TUC still backed Lib-Lab MPs until 1900 when it set up the Labour Representation Committee (LRC). After the Taff Vale Judgement in 1901, more unions supported the LRC and, by 1906, there were 26 Labour Party MPs. In Parliament, Keir Hardie continued to round on Tories and Liberals for their lack of sympathy for working people. He was no longer alone and both Parties were starting to sense the future, with some trepidation. On the Clee Hills, as in other working class communities, Keir Hardie's exploits were trumpeted loudly.

Walter and Joe are talking at the church gate. Joe has his brown and white, cross-bred terrier with him and Walter is knotting his red handkerchief to use as a head covering, having forgotten to bring his hat on this sunny, June afternoon.

"Have you heard the great news Walter? Our own man, Keir Hardie's gone to parliament wearing his cloth cap. It's a working man's cap he wears and it's put a shock up the top hat 'n tails lot, Liberals as well have turned their backs on him. To the devil I say with them all. This is the beginning Walter I tells you, only the beginning. We're on the way up at last! Even the Grand Old Man must be shaking in his boots."

"Gladstone's no spent force as yet Joe. He's a wily old dog-fox but I think we've made a good start. I shall give the stone a special thrashing tomorrow"

"While you're on it Joe, I've been wanting to ask you summat about the book. I've marked the page so just here first at page thirteen. I'll read it,

> *No sooner is the exploitation of the labourer by the manufacturer, so far, at an end, that he receives his wages in cash, than he is set upon by the other portions of the bourgeoisie, the landlord, the shopkeeper, the pawnbroker etc.*

So, shopkeepers are part of the boss class. But, just a few pages on, seventeen it is, it says,

The lower middle class, the small manufacturer, the shopkeeper, the artisan, the peasant, all these fight against the bourgeoisie, to save from extinction their existence as fractions of the middle class...

What should I make of it Joe? Is the shopkeeper part of it or against it, which is it?"

"That's a puzzle, Walter, a puzzle indeed. But I think I can square it off simple for you. What is meant is that, in the long run, the small shopkeeper has no future so he must fight but that, from our point of view as workers with nothing but our muscle to exchange for pounds and shillings, the shopkeeper appears to be another way of taking from us what is ours. This is one of the beauties of the book. It is not like the usual daft twaddle we gets to read. It demands you study it hard. And what is more, so I believe, is that it dares to say what the future will be, or at least could be once there's enough of us willing to raise the flag."

At this point, the rector loudly shuts the church door and crunches along the pathway in his high boots. Walter quickly secretes the good book inside a corduroy trouser pocket and Joe doffs his cap as the rector passes haughtily, sherry-veined snout to the skies, without so much as a word.

"He reminds me of a heron with a fat, bony chub stuck up its backside", offered Joe quietly with relish.

"I was thinking more of a crazy coot, Joe, or stuffed goose perhaps, but still with the fish up his rear, I think you've got that just about perfect, mate," replied the biscuit, "and it's a big one at that!"

"His ass or the chub?"

"Both. But, don't you think there might be something in it, Joe? After all, we don't know much about the world and the sun, the moon and what lies beyond. And the point of it all. Is it just possible that when we does die we shall rise into heaven like the vicar says?"

"Watty, my dearest friend, this is the addled talk I was referring to just a while ago. It's true that we don't know very much but, equally, that we knows a lot more than we did. And, furthermore, that, had we not taken the trouble to enquire, often against the express wishes of the churchmen, we should not be even as knowledgeable as we are. For instance, it was not so long ago that people believed the earth to be flat, so's a traveller who went too far would fall over the edge. No, the rector is earning a pretty penny peddling his nonsense."

"So, he is part of the boss class, Joe?"

"I'm certain that is true, as true as we can get, but there's more to it than that I fear....he, and all the other so-called religious people, are helping to keep folks like us with our noses pushed down in the gutter. "

"Is that so for the chapel? After all, they does good work and don't have their snotters pricked up so high."

"Yes, I believe it is so, Watty. The whole notion of it seems to be to put working people off the scent....to trick us into believing that our lot in this world doesn't really matter so much....which leaves the road wide open for them that already has plenty to pile it up even more. Chapel folk are good people, they're our class, that is true but they're still falling for it, just like the folk at the big church."

"But I knows the preacher has a soft spot for us, Joe. I can hear it in how he talks."

"Then would it not be better if he stood up for the poor but dropped all the hogwash, Watty? Certainly, he could include a word or two about the man, Jesus of Nazareth, the carpenter's son, as a good man who was not afraid to sit down with us lot. I can find no harm in that but there is no call to spin childish stories about him. It appears to me that such prattle takes away from his simple goodness...."

At that precise moment, Joe catches sight of the returning rector's bespectacled boat, ear cocked like a springer, from the corner of his eye,

"Why are you two men still here, idling at the lord's gate...and did I hear you mention his name? Have you nothing more useful to do? Get along to your homes now."

Walter felt his muscles tighten. For a split second he was sorely tempted to snap the man's scrawny neck. Joe was trying to back off with the semblance of a bow and fingers to forelock. The heron was getting annoyed, through habit oblivious to the danger he would be in had he not the backing of a hundred coppers and the rest.

"We wuz just wondering, like the two ign'rant fellows we is, how it might be we should raise our knowing about the world without seeming to go against what the bible says.."

"Stop right there, Walter Mann, it is not for the likes of you to question what the scriptures say, nor to query what your betters tell you is plainly so. We are already plagued by ridiculous notions...descended from monkeys we are said to be by Mr Darwin, for instance, such horse-tripe, and getting folk restless about their situation, but you would be far happier at home, tending to your garden or looking to your wife and children. These are not the thoughts for you. What benefit could they bring you? What harm might they cause should others take offence? Now move along both of you, and do so swiftly else you'll be sorry."

Walter, enraged and ready to despatch him, moved up close, one scuffed hobnail placed in between the rector's posh boots and breath steaming his lenses. At this awesome display, the illusion of safety left him like quicksilver. He was scared shitless and could not disguise the fact. A pungent odour was ample declaration of the trepidation he was experiencing and Watty's nose wrinkled up accordingly making his fearsome prospect even more terrifying at such close quarters. The rector was a coward. 'Half-crown to sixpence and sixpence to half-crown', as working people would quaintly say. Watty would have been foolish to press home the matter and he was never that. By the same token, it was a courageous thing to do, standing up against the churchman, with all his advantages of education and friends in high places. Similar examples of bravery could be found at that time in parliament. In June 1894, Keir Hardie called for the House of Commons to send a message of condolence to the relatives of 251 coal miners killed by an explosion in a colliery near Pontypridd in South Wales and that this should be added to an address of congratulations on the birth of a royal heir (the future Edward VIII). The request was refused and Keir Hardie made a speech attacking the privileges of the monarchy, creating uproar in the Commons and fury against Hardie in the newspapers. Such courage might be recalled by those who later ostracised him for his pacifism during the early part of the First World War (he died in 1915). Hardie was also in favour of women's suffrage, unlike some other Labour men. Like Walter, he was on the side of the angels and could also stand his ground in the face of great adversity.

CHAPTER FIVE

Quarryman and Poacher

Shropshire is fortunate in having abundant supplies of hard rock for use as road metal, paving 'setts', kerbing and gateposts. The world-renowned dolerite, known as 'dhustone' (which is sometimes hyphenated as 'dhu-stone') forms a weather resistant cap to the hills - Titterstone Clee Hill appears grander, because of its shape, although it is, in fact, slightly smaller (1749 feet) than the nearby Brown Clee Hill (1771 feet).

The stone fragments into cubical pieces which compress firmly together under a heavy roller. It does not smoothen easily, staying 'gritty' and thereby gives excellent foothold. There is little dust, good drainage and the dhustone also dries swiftly. Finally, its deposits are accompanied by coal seams used to power the necessary machinery. As well as the dhustone there were two granite quarries on Clee Hill, opened in 1867. By 1910, there were more than 70 quarries across Shropshire, employing a total of 1652 men and producing three quarters of a million tons of stone and clay (Watts, 1919, p.87). The workforce topped 2,000 according to later records and brought together men and their families from all over the country, especially the North East and Midlands.

Wielding a 28lb hammer or 'boster', Walter adeptly broke the hard dhustone. A person might spend all day attempting the same but, without a knowledge of just where to aim the blows, would fail miserably. Having reduced the rock to manageable proportions, Walter used a basket and wooden rake to load it onto trucks that were then pushed off on rails to the crusher. Dhustone, or dolerite, is an igneous rock, fine-grained like basalt and ideal for road metal chippings. As already mentioned, it tends to break into cubes but does sometimes produce acute edges and shards are notoriously sharp, like razors, and quarrymen are rarely un-blooded, sometimes an eye was taken by flying rock. 'Toe rags' were used inside the quarryman's boot to protect the feet from cutting. Strike breakers and management lackeys were also called 'toe rags' due to perceived similarities. 'Yarks' were the quarrymen's thick corduroy trousers, tied at the knee with string, worn in the quarries. The men worked in teams of three and, if one member should be injured and unable to work, then the other two had to carry the extra load. There was no help from the parish nor from government. Walter sweated cobs in those quarries. He gave his body each day to the hard labour but he was now holding back his soul. Of course, this is not to say that work was all-consuming. Fairer, perhaps, to say that survival was always top of the list and it is to Walter's out-of-work activities to that end that we shall now turn.

It is still said that Walter was the only man on the Clee Hills to have had the long nets out on Squire Whistler's front lawn. This was a dangerous thing to do because rabbit poaching was frowned upon, gamekeepers burly and squires to be feared, especially when they doubled as magistrates. Walter though was not easily put off his bunny. He was also up for the rough stuff if called upon and, it is told, had put many a bold gamekeeper in their 'bed' for the night, sometimes longer. Young Will Farlow would be sent ahead along the starlit hedge and, when the gamekeeper grabbed hold, Walter would lay him out with a single blow to the napper. Swinging a 28 pound sledge all day had certain advantages at such times and painful bandaged heads the end result. You could argue it was criminal but, equally, so was the hunger and grinding poverty endured every day by the ordinary people of the Clee Hills. Equally criminal too were the conditions inside Shrewsbury Gaol. Transportation to the colonies had officially ended in 1868 but six months in penal squalor at the Dana was still bad enough. Going hungry though amidst such plenitude was not considered an option for the likes of Walter and his accomplices.

"If I could get my hands on them they'd know trouble", said the bandaged man sitting in the Angel. In the adjoining bar, Walter and his crew forced back their chuckles.

Walter wore an open-necked shirt, without collar in all weathers. My father remembers his ginger chest hair, like bed-springs of copper wire and sparkling with snow as he returned from work. It is said that he would stand at the bar drinking his beer quietly and cause no trouble while rough-arsed quarrymen and miners were fighting all around him. Only extreme disorder would provoke him to act, usually by knocking two or more heads together before reclaiming his position. I have seen a photograph of him in his sixties when he was still an imposing figure.

In the summertime, Walter would join a group of hay-cutters who would service the local farms. No money changed hands, the favour returned in serving farmhouse cider any time in the year. Back-breaking work, sweat pouring and the green-eyed horse flies, called 'clegs', drawing blood as the men worked methodically across the fields, scythes expertly swinging in the sun. Some of the flies were larger, like grey moths, that could land on an exposed arm or neck without the victim feeling it. Lots of horses meant lots of flies. Then time for a much-needed rest. The sharpening stones would appear and a woman with a whisket holding a stone jar of cider arrive for the men's refreshment. Full body washing was a luxury and, as a consequence, the air ripe.

"You smell's like an old donkey, Walter Mann…just as well I'm all blocked up from the hay just now", teased Annie Thread's daughter Louisa.

Walter never batted an eyelid as he stroked his scythe expertly with a stone worn from many such outings. He paused to set his favoured clay pipe, first scratching out the 'swark' (tobacco residue) before chewing it, then filling the bowl with freshly-chewed 'twist' and lighting, then spitting with no little gusto. Louisa looked on amazed before continuing her address,

"Slovenliness is no part of religion and cleanliness is next to Godliness, says John Wesley and he ought to know something, so you're a disappointment both ways Walter, a double disaster I says".

Beyond his better judgement, Walter was moved to reply by this jesting impertinence. He switched his gaze to Louisa's and spoke softly to her,

"Such is cradle talk, my dear. I've a soft spot for Methodists, and John was a fine one so's I believe, but the very idea that the creator of the world and heavens should be concerned about such matters is indeed a nonsense. And, anyways, I can work as hard as any man, so 'slovenly' is not my habit. As for washing and such, I cannot see that God would care about such things. But, then, and I don't want to alarm you Louisa, such talk of God is surely fit only for the nursery. No such being could exist for, if it were so, where could he have himself come from? It solves no problem to say 'God'. It is a lazy, childish thing to say. Where do you imagine he might be from, Mamble is it, or maybe Cl'bry?"

"That's sacrilege to even breath it", shrills Louisa, "you should hang your empty yed in shame....and don't be riling me up with such questions...and 'gis that jar back so's I can pass it on, gis it here, you old goat..."

"My dear wench, but you said I was a donkey, just recent....how wondrous is the Lord that his most educated followers should change their beasts without so much as a blink of the eye", said Walter, losing the logic a little as he reluctantly handed over the cider and turned to walk his scythe again across the field, head, as was his custom, held high. Under his breath he repeated the words 'nursery tales' several times before his irritation subsided, his concentration shifting from the lines on his corduroy trousers to the diversity of life he was disturbing in the hay neatly falling to his blade.

Louisa meanwhile was making ready for the trek back across the hillside. She was thinking that Walter was getting too big for his britches, for a man who couldn't even sign his own name, and gutsed his food so loudly, and the Manns being no better, maybe even worse, than anybody else living at Titterstone Cottages. She kicked a tump of cut grass and spat before beginning her journey across the rough hillside, shifting to sheep-tracks where the main path was wearing thin or where a brook was cutting across it and the water too deep. A kestrel was hovering high above and skylarks above him sang their pretty songs, 'catch me if you can', thought Louisa. Soon she was hurrying along full of the joys and no longer concerned with the likes of Walter Mann.

Arriving at Titterstone Cottages, Louisa, now slightly out of breath, turns to look back fleetingly down the hill. Despite her parlous circumstances and prospects, she feels such intense love for her home and family that she could 'burst'. Deep sentiment she has too for her environment, presently green and, with such clement weather, a joy to behold. At other times, of course, this rugged landscape was anything but pleasant. Prolonged winter fogs, for example, often made it a bleak and treacherous world. Louisa decides to carry on her walk and so makes her way up steadily to the Bronze Age cairn, maybe 4,000 years old that stands close by the summit ofTitterstone Clee Hill.There is also an Iron Age hill fort, made of local stone, and, near the top, the 'Giants Chair' which is a precarious pile of boulders left behind in the Ice Age. In order to guide people across this wild terrain, a three-forked pole was erected.This was especially helpful in the snow but, even in the summer months, clouds could sit apparently fixed on Titterstone and produce an eerie underworld of shapes and sounds. Folk in Ludlow still predict the weather according to whether or not Titterstone 'has his hat on' while, beneath the cloud's cover, many a traveller has been spooked to distraction by what turned out later to be a lost cow or disturbed sheep.

All working people were treated harshly, no-one was spared and the weakest usually received worst. They were thought of as beasts of burden, in fact less than animals in many cases. Women like Louisa were expected to undertake hard physical work whatever and whenever. During menstruation there was little they could do to hide their condition, all that was available was a collection of rags to be stuffed into underpants and washed out away from men's eyes. 'Having the rags on' is a phrase used to this day to denote a woman's period. While their well-heeled contemporaries suffered swoons and vapours, working women carried heavy bags of coal on their backs, blood showing through their tattered clothing. Some would leave their beds to walk six miles to Tenbury Wells, for skivvying work at knobs' houses or whatever else they could find that needed a dawn start.Then back the six miles to a full day's domestic graft, up steep hills in all weathers, stopping perhaps only to gather corn left in the fields after the harvest or slake their thirst at an icy spring. That is how it was and, if you can bear to look honestly and with a bit of nous at how things are today, even in the so-called Western democracies, that is, to all intents and purposes, how it is now. Yes, the levels have changed but the gap has stayed the same or worsened. In essence, poverty isn't about absolutes such as having enough to eat. It *is* about inequalities between people and how this affects them, both rich and poor. The well-off are impoverished by inequality in the sense that they become distanced from their fellows and their humanity blighted by the need to maintain their privileged position. The poor are affected in a multitude of ways, some obvious, others less so. Consider the following instance, involving Walter's son John and his friend Jeffrey.

To this day, Ludlow May Fair continues to be an important event in the life of the town and surrounding villages and hamlets. John and Jeff have walked the six miles to spend a few coppers on the amusements. A black man is presented in a cage. The boys have never seen a black person before in the flesh and marvel accordingly. A bearded lady waits in her tent. John catches sight of a small handwritten poster advertising a race,

"Jeff, look here, this is just up your street, with a prize for the winner and second-placed."

He asks the time of a man throwing for a coconut, interrupting his concentration,

"Fuck off ya little shit", is all the reply John receives for his trouble. The man misses by a mile and walks off cursing like a trooper.

"Take no notice, lad, it's coming up to two o'clock, you've a quarter of an hour if you want to enter", a more kindly gent obliges.

At this, the pair are away, up Old Street like young hares and turning right towards the Castle Green. They arrive and

John urges Jeff up to the folding table to enter the race. This is an 'open to all-comers race', over one hundred yards. The prize money of one pound has attracted a good number of athletes including two prime sprinters from the Grammar School. The entry fee is sixpence, a sum which neither John nor Jeff possesses but this does not deter John's efforts,

"We don't have it but he's got no chance anyway, no chance, mister, so let him start, he won't even get as far as the finish..."

"Alright, young fella, I shall enter him, name?"

"Jeffrey, sir....Jeffrey Norman."

"Thank you, now fix this number thirteen on his back carefully and get along smartly to the line up over by the castle wall."

The lads arrive at the line-up and gain stares and laughter from the posh young men in their racing spikes and whites. Jeff has 'holy' shoes and takes his shirt off to reveal a skinny torso. He is fourteen years of age but small, under-developed and puny-looking. More laughter, followed by indifference as the tension mounts.

"Get yourself ready now, Jeff, and go like the clappers", urges John.

Jeff goes to the end of the line and ties his laces up tight. He is barely noticeable amongst the fine and proud specimens of assembled manhood. Some even sport sideburns and 'taches. What they don't know, however, is the speed that even a working lad of fourteen can develop running around the steep gradients of Titterstone Clee Hill. Jeff is fast, easily the best of this particular bunch. Despite his poor diet and untutored technique, he's a handful for all but the swiftest in the county. But what of the conditions and his parlous equipment? Well, rain is traditional when the May Fair is held in Ludlow and the grass is consequently slippery. Spikes are a must but Jeff doesn't have them. Even so, he could still take first prize.

As the gun cracks, the race is underway, Jeff slipping, slower at first but then picking up the pace and he's alongside the leaders, flying, gasping for breath, then his confidence goes and shoulders stiffen, through the tape....third. Third place is creditable. For someone so young, naïve and lacking, third is bloody amazing. But Jeff was actually the fastest in the field that day. The reason he didn't scoop the prize was down to his lowly expectations of himself. He did not believe he could, maybe that he should, win. Once that belief took proper hold, his dash was defeated.

"Well done lad, offers one of the rich boys", in a slightly patronising tone.

"Jeff, what held ya back?" is John's query, as the two pals head off past the Crimean War cannon into the market.

"Fuck 'em, John, I had a go, they're all big lads, full grown men some of 'em..."

"You showed 'em, Jeff, and them with such fancy outfits and all them spiked racing shoes...you with just your old plodders on, third is good, very good and your folks 'ill be pleased with ya, and no danger they won't, I'm telling ya."

They cross the Bull Ring and head for home, at a measured jog to begin and faster as the thought of home and telling everyone the news gains hold. In the Feathers Hotel, back in Ludlow, the race winner is having a drink, enjoying the fireside warmth, merry company and pleasant surroundings. In the back of his mind, however, there is just the beginning of a doubt, but it doesn't last long. The pressures to assume and attractions of assuming supremacy are all around, after all.

As the Victorian era reaches its last few years, Walter and family are well-settled at Titterstone Cottages, a short row of 'two-up-and-two-downs' standing at the top of a steep bank. From here, Walter has a short walk to work. The house has a good-sized back garden that is fully exploited – spuds, cabbages, sprouts, onions and beans being the main vegetables produced. The family's pig lives in a sty at the bottom and is fed anything and everything. The neighbours are easy-going and quiet. Walter and Mary now have five children, their second daughter, Caroline, being born in 1898, but still no great number compared with other families nearby. The chimney smoke rises lazily although all is about to change.

CHAPTER SIX

Betrayed by a Cousin

The beginning of the twentieth century sees the birth of Walter's favourite child, Mary but is also a time of great torment for the Mann family. By the summer of 1901, Walter had been sentenced to prison and was accommodated in Shrewsbury Gaol. Situated near the Severn and called the 'Dana' after an earlier prison on the site, this is located on Howard Street in Shropshire's county capital. But, before we join Watty in the nick, let us take a look at how he got there.

Into the Greyhound Pub comes red-faced Ted Hicks,

'Walter's been taken by the rozzers, lads! He's been nabbed red-handed, plum,with the nets, up near the squire's place, near the spring. I told him not to chance it so close to that sneaky bastard's place. Hired hands…some rogues from Mamble and a constable or two. They 'ad revolvers and shotguns, armed to their rotting teeth, 'n a pich fark, damn their eyes. Walter 'ad to put his hands up but young Will got away, thank God…he climbed the bannut (walnut tree) and then on a branch to jump the ditch and he's away in the dark….one of the dogs was shot, though, and the old Ginger Biscuit's bin taken first off to Ludla lock-up, then onwards to Soosbri and they says he'll be at the Dana before the week's out and set certain for a long stretch. The squire's got it in for 'im so the boys at the Angel are saying. It's a bad do, indeed. We'll 'ave to make sure Mary and the rest's properly provided for.'

"How did they know to catch 'em there? That's what I wants to know. Wust there when he was taken Ted?" queried Bert Miller through the snug doorway.

"I wusna, Bert, but I heard it from an old girl who knows Will's 'alf sister Myra. She was waitin a visit from the law being as they appeared to know who they was after."

"He's a chancer and no mistake, taking rabbits from there, he's delivered himself into the hands of the meanest man on the Clee Hills, why didna 'e lay the nets up near the quarry, there's plenty a rabbits there?"

"Ah but Watty prefers a better class of bunny", cackled in one of the Miller boys, sprawling half-cut next to the fire, "he was not to be so satisfied with flea-ridden second raters, like's as what we 'ave to be contented with. No, he wants to taste proper warren rabbit, as enjoyed by the top knobs and suchlike."

At this Ted let fly, "...'n you can shut yer trap 'n all, crawl back up yer pipe, Watty's worth a dozen of the likes of you."

"Ted's right there, says Bert hoping to quieten his unruly brood, "but we munna fall out amongst ourselves over this lads, we've all done daft tricks and I smells summat rank 'ere, somebody has twitted, you ask me...what does you think 'bout it, Joe?"

It was Albert Watson he was referring to, Walter's secret mentor sitting quiet,

"Has anyone new been noticed?" Joe asks, and what about any new fellas at the quarry? There's Eddy Fenshaw...but he seems a good 'un...and Walter's cousin Bill started last month but nobody else as I can recall."

"I can't see it being family who done it, Joe, not family."

But, of course, as anyone could guess from reading this, it was indeed family, in the very person of William Mann.

When he arrived at the Dana, Walter was two'd up and shared a piss-pot with Edward Griffiths from Church Stretton who had been caught stealing cabbages and other similar produce from rich people's gardens. The cell was dingy, cramped, damp and cold but both men were used to roughing it so that wasn't what mattered. The worst was being shut indoors, this is what made it a punishment, especially for Walter. Day-times he was put to work in the yard breaking hard stone brought from the nearby quarries but this was a stroll for a man so intimately familiar with the dhustone. When there was no work to do, he lay on his bed, listening to the cries of boat-men at work on the nearby River Severn. The railway station was also close and steam trains coughed and hissed their way up to Crewe or down to Hereford. Walter spent many empty hours dreaming of the view from the bonk, across the Shropshire plain to the Black Mountains of Wales. Or down by the River Teme at Ludford, on market days. Searching for crayfish under the slippery brown stones. Then along to Whitcliffe and the 'bread-walk' with its strange fossils in the limestone rocks that tumbled down the steep slopes. Watching a brown trout rising to a fly struggling on the water's surface. Of course, Watty pined for Mary most nights and even missed the twins after a while. Towards the end of his sentence, he had occasion to visit the surgeon who lanced a carbuncle on his backside. Boils, spots and skin diseases were common because of the poor diet, lack of sunlight and other manky conditions that prisoners endured. Walter and 'Ted' would often talk at lights out,

"Why'd they make such a fuss over a few rabbits Walter? You only dun it to feed the family and help look after folk who was out of work."

"Way I sees it, Ted, is that they wants ta own everything,

the lot, before they can ever be happy. Specially the country rich. They're a particular breed and have a peculiar point of view about it. It's as if the land and all that grows and lives upon it belongs to them. So, when we takes the nets out on the land it's like we's pissing on their best carpet, wazzing away, say, in their drawing room."

"But they don't care a bugger about the land or anythin' living on it for that matter. I'm shamed having to admit it but I used ta follow the hunt and I've seen the toffs do some wicked business to poor foxes and whatever else the hounds got hold of. I saw 'em savage a young falla deer once up by where the Corve joins the Teme, it's neck hanging out screaming, and the fuckin' gentry, women riders and all, laughing at the agony while they drained their silver cups. They're bloody bastards, Walter, that's the only words for 'em, bastards. And they wants sorting out 'n bringing down a peg or two."

Ted draws breath while Watty listens on,

"…'n then they're in church, kneeling and praying, and swanking as they parades in to their appointed pews, and the meek and mild shall inherit the earth, and the vicar and bishop is pissing in the same pot, what bollucks is that! If Jesus, son of a carpenter as he was so's we're told, was ta see 'em in their fineries then he'd have a fuckin' fit about it. He'd tell 'em to cut their daft cackle and help us poor buggers." Another pause from Ted and then,

"Walter, you're indeed a man after my own heart and I'm as pleased as a dog with two dicks to be sharing this meagre cell with ya."

At this moment, one of the screws kicks the door and shouts for them to shut the noise. Watty whispers 'fuck off' into his mattress and Ted offers the traditional single finger salute.

"That's the bastard who broke Bill Tidy's back through

turning the screw to full", says Ted, then explaining to Watty how hard hard labour can be when you're working the treadmill.

"I should like to meet the man one day, Ted, I should sorely enjoy that moment".

"Shut the rattle you two", shouts the screw and the two compatriots in crime settle down for the long night ahead.

New prisoners are sectioned off to be addressed by the Governor, Mr Norman H. Mitchell-Innes and his Principal Warder, S.D.Fennell whose leading initials were always separated by an 'O' by the inmates and, indeed, by many of his underlings. The chaplain, the Reverend William George Dimock Fletcher is in attendance, as are John Davies Harries, surgeon and H. Bell the storekeeper. The Governor is already well into his stride,

"Our prison was built by England's greatest architect, Mr Thomas Telford, over a period of six years at the end of the last century. Over the gateway you will possibly have noticed a bust of Mr John Howard, the noted philanthropist and friend of prisoners….."

Walter's attention is now distracted, fascinated by the surgeon who is swaying from side to side, pissed as a newt. The Reverend notices Walter's averted gaze and glares at him. The drone continues,

"The prison has a total of 204 cells, 179 for men, which leaves 25 for females…for those of you who can count…plus a small number of apartments for debtors. Something you should know is that the Justices visit the prison monthly…."

There is a sharp retort in the ranks caused by the forced breaking of wind. A sound somewhere between tuba and horn, with hints of an accompanying top trumpet for the discerning listener. Small but discernible spaces clear around the culprit.

The Governor pauses briefly and a flicker of disgust passes across his well-whiskered face.

Later Fennell is left to march the men across the yard back to their cells,

"You bastards won't get fed enough to fart," he mutters coldly.

Before the Prisons Act of 1868 hangings were conducted in public, afterwards they were held inside prison walls. Henry Pierrepoint from Lancaster had his first lead role as hangman (he had assisted previously) at Shrewsbury Gaol on Tuesday 18th August 1900. He hanged Richard Wigley (who had murdered his landlady), aged thirty-nine years, who was then buried in an unmarked grave inside the prison. Henry was later sacked because he arrived for a hanging in Sudbury, Suffolk, in July 1908 'considerably the worse for drink' and, apparently, had also been involved in a fight the preceding afternoon. Hanging people had its consequences. It played havoc with Henry's sleeping and he became steadily less even-tempered.

"I swear I heard the crack of his neck this morning, Ted, they hung him early this cold, wet morn, I bet he was shaking like a babe."

"They say he's a new hangman, Walter. Henry Pearponce from up north, I think that's what they calls him and this was his first neck stretching as top man. They've put Dick in an unmarked grave just by the Severn-side wall, not even a bloody flower or wooden cross for him."

"I'll bet he won't miss 'em, Ted. Where he's gone, he won't be missing anyone or anything, you can be sure of that."

In prison, so the story goes, it's best to keep your head down and your nose out of other men's affairs. You don't ask questions. Especially about what crime was committed but other things too are practically taboo. Of course, this is only true in part. It applies mainly to prisoners who don't know one another. Walter and Ted got on well and this allowed a much more open conversation between them. Walter, was interested to find out what Ted had done for a job before he was nabbed and so he asked him outright,

"What was your line of work then, Ted? I hope you don't mind me asking and I shan't take offence if you tells me to mind my own."

"No, that's alright Watty, I was a gravedigger for many years. I started out on the farm, sheep and cattle work mostly but then I got a job digging homes for dead folk!"

"That's hard work, Ted, I know because I've dug one or two myself, helping out the regular man at Coreley for a few pennies, and, I've sweated buckets...'specially where the ground's never 'bin broken before or if it's hard frozen in wintertime."

Ted did not ask Walter about his occupation. He was still not sure enough of the big man. That's how it can be inside. Besides, Ted had been raised in the grubber (workhouse) where you were well-prepared for later, institutional life. Don't ask too many questions if you know what's good for you. Watty, however, pursued his questioning and moved to the more sensitive matter of crimes committed,

"So what was you nicked for, Ted? Again, tell me to keep me snout out if I'm pushin' it."

"No, Watt, that's no bother at all. I was caught with a couple of cabbages and a pocketful of radishes in the local knob's vegetable garden, just trying to feed the family."

Watty holds back a titter, his eyes on fire with amusement.

" Truth told, I'd been at it for most of the summer, lettuce here, a root of spuds, runner beans and a few sticks of rhubarb maybe."

"The rhubarb rustler, interjects Watty, laughter exploding across his face."

Ted whacks him hard on the shoulder and the two enjoy the moment, a rare occasion in the Dana.

"Right then, Mr Smartbolluck, let's be hearing how you earned your ticket inside?" asks Ted once the ribaldry subsides.

"Well Ted, like you, I've had to bring in a bit extra to keep the young 'uns fed proper and I'd had the nets out many a night to catch a rabbit or two. This one night me and Will had just started home when we was jumped by half a dozen likely so-and-sos, tooled up to the nines and meaning to do bad business if called upon. I made sure the lad got away but they had me held and bound before I could get enough leverage in my punches. They were tough boys, anyway, and I took a right thumping. Not that I'm complaining about it though, it's no less than what I expects and I've done my fair share myself. What I can't fathom is how they was all there waiting and so sure I'd be there? That's the riddle I can't crack."

"Sounds like you was let down by someone who knew…somebody close I shouldn't wonder, Watty?"

"But who Ted, who? I can't recall telling anyone and Will knows how to keep his trap shut."

"It must be from him, Watty, if it's not himself who done it...he must have given you away, maybes not knowingly but I reckons it came from your lad."

Ted was right. Will had given the game away, albeit inadvertently, by getting the long nets out from under the stairs and taking them up to the top of the garden. He'd been seen doing it by one of the Millers who'd mentioned it at the Dhustone Inn, just in passing but loud enough to reach the attentive ears of William Mann, one of Walter's relatives, who was on his way to Ludlow. William and Walter were on bad terms and William had heard that Squire Whistler was looking to catch poachers, in particular the ones who'd been so bold as to have the nets out on his lawn. It was too good an opportunity for William to pass up and he knew a couple of characters in Mamble who would alert the Squire's men and provide the extra muscle required for Watty's capture. The deed was done and Watty's future set out for him.

Walter, though, is now due for release, first thing tomorrow morning, as it happens. A Monday that was long-coming. Sunday chapel service at the Dana was cold and bleak but Walter and Ted were pleased to have something different to do, whatever it might be. The chaplain, known as 'Dim' to the inmates, has selected some choice extracts from Genesis to spout this morning,

"And God called the light day, and the darkness he called night..."

"And a clever fella, he must have been to know such things", mutters Ted while Watty has to pinch himself hard to stop laughing out loud.

"I bet he could name the days of the week as well, Monday he called Monday, Tuesday..." continued Ted, working hard on Watty's resolve.

"Will you shut your gob", pleads the Biscuit.

The chaplain stops and clears his throat, with a glance towards the audience, aware of the chatter but not of its precise origin. This gives Watty the chance to steady himself while giving Ted a sharp prod to the rib-cage.

Before following Walter's release and return home, we should consider the culprit behind, and circumstances leading up to, his incarceration. As can be imagined, there was many a heated conversation in Ludlow and on the Clee Hills over the years as to who was responsible for tucking him up so nicely with the law. Only one man, apart from the two rogues from Mamble sworn to secrecy, knew who it was and he was the one who'd done it. His name was William Mann and he was Walter's second cousin, a year older but only half the physical proportion and with a grudge to end all grudges. He was born at Claverley in Shropshire and, unlike Walter, he began his working life in agriculture. More precisely, he worked as a general servant on John Tongue's farm, the 'Thatch' at Sidbury. The reason for William's hatred was that he had once courted Mary Harmison, Walter's future wife. A month or so after Walter's incarceration, William knocks on Mary's door, it's after dusk and the nights are drawing in,

"Will, where have you bin hiding, I've not seen you since Watty was put away?"

"That's right Mary, I've been lodging with a mate of mine in Soosbri, just in case Watty needed me you see but I cunna stay there no longer, one reason or another..I was wondrin' if I could lodge here for a while, just until I can find somethin' more permanent. I'd be working at the quarry and see you alright for board and that."

With money tight and mouths to feed, Mary is in a predicament, mindful of her history with William and, of course, Walter's likely view on the matter,

"Come in....I reckon we should be talking it through first, given as how we've known each other pretty well in the past," she says, looking to see who might be watching. Will pushes in. The family are sitting in the front room, their faces picked up in the lamp-light and flickers from the fire. Edwin Fenshaw is the lodger, a quarryman, aged twenty-five, standing by the window. A young widow, Louisa Thread and her two year old son are also staying. Walter and Mary's daughter Sarah, aged fourteen, is there although only visiting from the 'big house' where she works as a servant. Louisa is unable to pay anything towards her keep but Mary can't see her without a roof over her head. The house is already more than full but Mary needs the extra income and so William is allowed to stay.

"You're a pretty sight now then Sarah," smiles and tobacco teeth from Will. There was already an inevitability about his abuse of her and it was only a matter of months before it happened. Mary saw it right there and then but knew she could do nothing to stop it. Inevitable given the conditions. There was little privacy nor protection. Anyway, such things were far from uncommon on the Clee Hills, or anywhere else for that matter. Girls and women were customarily treated like property, often not so well. In the worst communities, teenage pregnancies were ubiquitous and stories about 'sharing the babies out at Christmas' not uncommon. Caroline, Watty and Mary's second daughter, herself had two illegitimate children who, as it happens, went on to do very nicely for themselves.

The copulative event itself was rough, sordid, dismal and grubby. A silent, grudging acquiescence from Sarah without any hint of the engaged compliance frequently found in men's tales and fantasies. And yet from such hurried and fumbling transgression, a child was conceived who would bring such gladness to Sarah and the rest of the family. At four months the baby was clearly showing and Mary had noticed that Sarah. had not suffered 'the curse' for a while. There was some straight talking, tears aplenty and then Mary took her disgust and anger out on William with an old piece of blackened chisel steel she used to break the coal. He was off back to Claverley one early morning, nursing two broken fingers and a lump the size of a coot's egg on the side of his head. He deserved far worse and, if Watty had ever come to know about what had gone on while he was away, no doubt would have received it in full measure.

Mary knew to hold her tongue because Watty wouldn't have stopped to consider the consequences. There would have been a bloody murder and then what? Keeping quiet was all she could reasonably do in the circumstances.

Sarah's boy was always her pride and joy. He was accepted as part of the household and no distinctions were ever made. It mattered nothing to her that he was fatherless, they were both much better off without William Mann, she thought.

Walter was released from prison in April 1902. He trudged the long miles back to his beloved Titterstone, stopping the first night in a barn with the cows and then moving on south, tickling a small brown trout in the river Onny one cold morning for his breakfast. Cooked over an old hawthorn fire, giving it a wonderful flavour and so easily done when you know how. A day was spent near 'The Bog', a mine taking high quality lead ore from the Stiperstones Hills. This marked a slight diversion from his pathway home but he had promised to call in on Ted's wife Marge and their seven children, just to say he was doing fine and looking forward to being released in the first week of July that year. The family had been obliged to move from Shrewsbury having lost their breadwinner and, consequently, their lodgings. Marge and Ted's eldest boy was earning a wage shifting the ore and this, coupled with a few bob from Marge's skivvying, kept things afloat. Watty himself was only too glad to do his friend a favour and slept comfortably enough for an hour or so in the family's shed, in spite of the scampering rats and a rustling 'hedge pig', as the hedgehog was called in those days. Then, on again to the bonk, heart racing as he crossed Ledwych Brook at Henley and beginning the steep climb homewards. Mary and two of the kids met him on the bank just before the big holly tree, where badgers were said to wait for the unwary child returning from school in wintertime.

A joyous reunion was had. Watty was too excited to sleep and the bed too comfortable anyway, after prison's privations. Mary had her man back and there would soon be good money coming in again.

The Anglo-Boer War ended shortly afterwards. Now picture the scene, if you will, a candle-lit public bar at the Royal Oak. Bob 'Two Stripes' Keyes, a corporal in the 2nd Kings Shropshire Light Infantry, has just returned from an army hospital in South Africa after being shot in the foot by a Boer sniper.

"It was the biggest army you can imagine…there was lads from all over, Welsh, Irish and Scots, there was one fella in the Black Watch….used to be a cruel 'un. Seemed to enjoy his work a little too much. He often told tales of how he had shot the Boer women and children, just for looking wrongly at him. And the natives, the poor blacks, he had even less mercy for them. They was fodder for his rifle. A cruel cunt he was."

"War's war Bob, it cunna ever be said to be pretty. Besides, I wouldn'a of necessity go by every thing a jock told me," said one of the Brimfield boys.

"You've a point there, Tom, but I seen sights that would make you weep, great camps of civvies, all behind barbed wire and the conditions worse than we would house a mangy dog…some of 'em was no more than skin and bone, it makes me sad to say. It was a wrong thing to do to helpless people, ordinary people they was at the end of the day, just like you and me, and most of the dead was children."

"But we prevailed, Bob, we beat 'em square in the end and now it's our land and we shall bring some order to a godless wilderness."

"We lost five times as many men as they did, Tom, they fought like they meant it, like we should fight if they came to our backyards….think what we should give 'em if they came up here on Clee Hill, we knows every track and pathway, every mineshaft and hiding place….though we slaughtered twenty thousand or so of their folk in the camps on top of what soldiers we killed. Thinking on it, I would say the union flag is there to mark our claim to the gold that lies in the streams and rivers and hills, nothing else. That was told me by a clever lad by the name of John Wilks who comes from over near Bayton, he was a private in the 1st Worcesters...he used to cause a stir amongst the corporals and sergeants, even some of the officers used to pay him heed, given his command of the regulations and...well, it was more that he knew how to put things over in the right words...and they knew he could wrap them up tidy if he wanted to so's they left him be once they found he was a tough lad as well and wouldn't be broken by giving him fatigues, drill and the like...and then he used to sing songs and cite poetry that he'd made up himself. We laughed ourselves daft many a time, believe me, sitting round the fire, smoking our pipes and listening to his banter. He could take the rise out of the boss class famously and he used to cuss like you've never heard. I shouldn't like to repeat some of the lingo! He was a private just like us but he was from a well-to-do family and he'd been disowned by his family through too much of a liking for the perry."

"That stuff makes I shit," a different Brimfield observes emphatically.

"…and they had been real well off. He could read 'n write and signed his name like a school-teacher. He said that was the reason behind the war. And I believes him."

"That sounds cuckoo-talk, Bob, we has no need for such trifles given what we already has. King and country, remember this is the greatest empire that has ever been or shall ever be…"

Walter has held his tongue up to now but, unable to restrain himself any longer, he jumps in at this point with a passion,

"Having plenty is no reason for our greedy government to hold back, lad. Even some of the Liberals, like Lloyd George, was against the war and said it was unfounded. Think of the brave men who fell so as rich 'uns could line their pockets even more. And how much of the gold would ever come to the likes of us? Tell me. The only good thing to come from the war was that it showed how desperate a life is for the working man. A good half of them what tried to enlist was not allowed to join on account of being too poorly or weak, unfit for service, with rickets and suchlike. That caused a rumpus and things will have to be done before it's forgot about."

At this, the dispute settles like dust in the rain, with all parties seeing the sense of Walter's point and none wishing to take him on when his dander was up with such a vehemence. Conversation returned to more prosaic matters - rising prices, ferrets and football. Bob was invited to display his wound once more, the Brimfields shared their appraisals of the new bar-maid and Watty was rewarded for his astute intervention with having to finance a round of beers and ciders. As he made his way to the bar, Watty felt warmly pleased with himself; he was becoming much more confident at making his point at such times, he knew where he stood and could find a way of bringing members of his class together. Joe would be proud of him.

It would be reckless of me to finish this chapter without at least passing reference to the momentous year of 1905. Momentous because of the achievements of, perhaps, the greatest scientist who has ever lived, Albert Einstein. In that year, Albert not only uncorked his special theory of relativity, 'supplanting Newtonian ideas', but also provided an explanation of Brownian motion, 'the most powerful evidence for the existence of atoms (Chown, 2006; pp. 5-7). It would be difficult to imagine a more productive twelve months! Of course, such world-shifting developments went by unnoticed by Watty and, arguably, everyone else living on the Clee Hills at that time. And, that is precisely the point to be made here because things could and should have been very different! Imagine an educated working class, freed from the mental prisons of religion, nationalism, monarchy etcetera. Imagine a community of intellectuals and scholars dedicated to empowering their fellows rather than accept the bribes and back-handers of capitalists, resting comfortably in their beds while such ignorance and suffering prevailed. A hundred years later and working people are still served pap and there are probably more brown-nosed scoundrels in high places than ever. And, without wanting to take on any airs and graces, I have a sneaking suspicion that dear old Albert, who liked an idea that initially appeared strange or impossible, would probably agree with me! Of course, the world could be different.

CHAPTER SEVEN

Walter's Later Years and Demise

In the summer of 1907, Watty celebrated his fortieth birthday. Despite being built like a battleship, he was already starting to feel some of the agonies of age, especially in his hands, shoulders and back. Lifting and carrying heavy stone, bending double and the effects of swinging the bolster all added up to a later life of chronic pain. Being outdoors at the rock-face in all weathers also took its toll. In the burning heat of mid-summer and through the blizzards of January and February, Walter broke the hard dhustone and his physical well-being inevitably suffered. On a wider canvas, there was some measure of recognition that the health of the working population should be improved, although real progress was terribly slow for Titterstone folk. Conditions were bleak, doctors still reluctant to travel and, although Ludlow Hospital opened in 1907, it was seen as a last resort for only the most desperate.

It is May 1912 and George V has been on the throne for just two years and the Clee Hills are a hive of industry. Walter is still working at the quarry face. The crushed stone is sent in trucks down the incline to join the rail network for distribution. Mat Griffiths is both a Great Western Railways engineer and shop steward for the Hereford branch of his union. He has been asked by the quarry owners to advise on the use of larger trucks which is not a simple matter, given the steep slope and shallow foundations of the track-way. Mat is talking with a small group of quarryman, including Walter, as they enjoy their bait,

"'Bin a while since I seen you last, Watty," says Mat warmly.

"Now then Mat, how goes it with the union, any news since we last met?"

"Matters are improving, I would say. Now we no longer have to pay for our MPs, since the government took on that responsibility, men have been more willing to join up. You will recall Mr Osborne's complaint that was upheld at the House of Lords – he was a Liberal man that worked on the railways and disagreed with having to pay towards the Labour party through his subscription to the A.S.R.S."

"But you still backs Labour MPs, Mat, I know you does..."

"That's right, Watty, but it's a different set-up nowadays. We only helps them out with their expenses and suchlike, it's the government that pays their wages. Anyway, how about you lads, have you joined up yet?"

"We've had to sign saying we won't join Mat, or else we'll be getting the push..."

At this, the hooter sounds and the quarrymen trudge back to their labours. Later that same day, Ernest Hicks is badly injured in a rock-fall. Tons of stone fall from the face and he is lucky to come out of it alive. Ernest suffers nasty fractures of wrist and leg and is unable to work for many months, during which time Watty covers his job as well as his own. Some days Watty cries inside with the strain of it. He longs for a different world and, despite the strong community of which he is a part, often feels all alone. There is no trade union to assist him. Are there no rich folks who can see the injustice of it all? Sadly, not. On the other hand, as the years pass, there are some stirrings of change. On Sundays, young socialists from the towns travel out to country areas on bicycle, singing and giving talks. Sometimes they stick posters in strange places to gain attention,

"Watty, cum 'n see this! Some daft young 'uns from Ludla have put a poster on one of the Pritchett's cows. They're talking about changing things for us poor buggers again…"

"And about time it would be if we did get our fair share" Watty says in reply to Ned the blacksmith. "I know we dunna always agree, Ned, but…"

"People can get themselves killed", interrupts Ned sharply. "I've the woman who stopped the Derby in mind."

On the 4th June 1913, Emily Davidson throws herself at the King's horse Anmer at the Derby. She dies from a fractured skull a few days later. The horse is destroyed and its jockey badly hurt. 'Deeds not words' is a suffragette slogan and most apt.

"But Ned, what else are women to do if every lawful way forward is blocked against 'em, every road barred, what can they do but throw themselves into the fray?"

"That's a child's mother. Or somebody's daughter, Watty, real flesh and blood. You canna play so reckless with folk in such ways. How would you feel if Mary was to take up with 'em? I doubt you'd be so much in favour then."

"Their fight is ours, Ned, so's if Mary wanted to take it up I should be alongside her, no matter what people might say. It can never be right to deny women the right to vote, to have a say in who their masters should be, it canna be right..."

"These things takes time, Watty, rushing like a bull at a gate only ends in..."

"A busted gate", the Biscuit completes Ned's sentence for him, much to his annoyance which he shows by giving Watty a playful punch to the shoulder.

"Don't forget about your job", Ned continues..."and missus and kids to clothe and feed, Watty...none of us can afford that round here. All the gaffers know one another and word gets round if you're a trouble-maker".

"Let me ask you, Ned. What would you do if rich 'uns told you you couldna vote?"

"But that's not going to ever happen, is it, working men would never stand that, there'd be bloody riots, hell to pay..."

"Exactly that, Ned, and you'd be there and I'd be there whatever got chucked at us. We'd have to fight and that's how it is now for women and good socialists who supports 'em. Once they gets the vote, 't'will be like they've always 'ad it and you would fight to 'elp 'em should somebody try to take it away."

"You shan't convince me, Watty, whatever way you puts it and not to mention your easy way with words. I knows what you're getting at and you knows how stubborn I is…now, let's be finding Jack Ringley, he's a horse for sale and I've a likely buyer for it in mind."

When war broke out, Walter had recently celebrated his forty-seventh birthday so was not called up. He was not sorry, even in the mad early days of 1914 because of what he knew. He was appalled by how readily the young men from the quarries and mines flocked to fight their fellow German workers. He had held his tongue when Keir Hardie spoke out vehemently against the war, splitting the labour movement into rival factions. Walter guessed that the time was unripe for such talk, that patriotism was still the stronger force. As the slaughter progressed, as men began to return to the Clee Hills, bandaged and broken, the mood changed. Any remaining jingoism was likely to receive short shrift from the bereaved and bloodied families who were obliged to pick up the bill.

A cold February afternoon in 1915 and Walter's daughters Sarah and Mary are standing patiently on Ludlow Railway

Station platform to meet the train bringing back men from the Western Front. Sarah is longing to see her husband, Ernest, again. She already knows he has been seriously wounded but, as he is helped off the train by another soldier, her heart drops like a stone. She turns away and cries into her hand at the sight of him. Bayoneted through the eye and ear – the third and likely, fatal thrust from his German assailant had been stopped by two shots from an officer's revolver – mustard gassed and frozen in the trenches, 'Ernie' was lucky to be alive and no prospect for a lover's eyes. He later developed diabetes and became an invalid for long periods but still worked as an outside porter at a posh Ludlow Hotel, using pony and trap to transport rich folks to and from the station. The twins Peter and John, were both gassed and returned home in the summer. Young Walter had his arm blown off by an artillery shell. He became very ill and his wife was soon unable to cope with his care, given that she also had four children to raise. Young Walter later dies, in his sister Mary's arms, of pernicious anaemia. It was a cruel war and, for ordinary people, the effects on family and community were especially harsh.

Men from the Clee Hills continued to be called up and Watty thought once or twice about enlisting, regardless of his age. He had heard, anyway, that coal miners were being drafted into the army to work as 'tunnellers' and that Tommy 'Whippet' Upham, his old mucker from Highley pit, had already joined up. The idea was to tunnel under your opponent's trenches and then blow him sky-high. This was not seen as particularly sporting by either side and, as a result, tunnellers were doubly unpopular. Not for the first or last time, the Germans enjoyed the initial successes and the British caught on later. Word was that men were paid three times as much as an ordinary private and that it didn't matter how old a man was as long as he'd plenty of experience underground, in the mines or digging sewers! Tommy would later be killed somewhere between Ypres and Paschendale, although his body was never recovered. He had been tunnelling under the German lines when the roof had collapsed and buried him in Flanders clay. When Walter presented himself ready for service he was rejected without a reason being given to him. He suspected it might be because of his age, even though other fifty years olds served in what was called '171 Company' or, perhaps, because of his size which might have caused difficulties in the tiny spaces in which the men had to work. Whatever the reason, Watty was obliged to continue his quarrying work on Titterstone Clee Hill.

Watty took great comfort from the Communist Manifesto, 'the real bible' as he would call it in safe company. On Sundays he would often consult its wisdom and certain phrases would stay with him throughout the week. "The working men have no country" was a favourite of his during the war years, helping him to resist the tide of hatred and daily calls for revenge against Germany. But, there were other parts of the book which caused him no little consternation: he agonised with page 71 which instructs that,

> *"Bourgeois marriage is in reality a system of wives in common and thus, at the most, what the Communists might possibly be reproached with is that they desire to introduce, in substitution for a hypocritically concealed, an openly legalised community of women..."*

Walter could grasp the idea that rich men saw poor people, just like they did animals, as existing solely for their own purposes and pleasures because he had observed the effect of this many times. He thought back to master Blunt's callous use of Sam

Pritchard in the churchyard, which was an obvious case. Then there were women who were obliged to sell their bodies in order to live. But, he was also aware of more subtle manifestations. Like the way his mother Caroline and sister Sarah were treated by their employers. It wasn't just because they were poor. It was because they were poor women that made it so. But what could 'a system of wives in common' mean? Was it that powerful men saw all women as their own? Even the wives of other rich men?

He turned back to the book, working his way down the page,

> *"For the rest, it is self-evident that the abolition of the present system of production must bring with it the abolition of the community of women springing from that system, i.e. of prostitution both public and private."*

This was hard for Walter because he loved Mary with all his heart. It was not in his nature to disrespect her. He had been raised to treat all women as 'his sister'. How could his marriage to her be a 'prostitution'? This was a cruel thing to even think. But then what was meant by 'marriage'? What was expected of a married woman? That she must surrender herself to her husband's desire, yes, but not to other men, to whom she was not married. But, then, once she had been married then she was placed in a different category and, should she lose her spouse, she would remain in that grouping. The word 'widow' would offer some protection but she would still be 'available' once a certain period of time had elapsed. Perhaps, this was it. But, there again, men got married too. Was it the same? His brain tormented him and he it. He would seek out Joe once more. Joe would certainly know the answer and, of course, he did,

"See Watty, it's not so much about whether you loves her or whether you don't. Like my own dear Catherine, your Mary cunna be regarded as an equal in the marriage. For one thing, she cunna even cast her vote. She has no say, in the way you and I does, about who should govern us. A war is underway in France and it will take every bit a strength for this country to prevail, and I hope it does, but it will likely require the wholehearted endeavour and many lives of women as well as men to the cause. It is also the case that the children are your children, they are yours in a similar sense to how property belongs to you. Inspite of the fact that Mary carried 'em, brought 'em into the world and fed 'em at her own tit, they belongs to you!"

"I dunna fully understand such things, Joe, though I've heard that Mr. Keir Hardie has called for women to have the vote."

"There is talk that our dear Scottish friend and ally is a-bed, poorly and unlikely to see the year out."

Now Watty starts to demonstrate the progress he has made in regards to thinking about socialism, alongside a new-found confidence that allows him to question his mentor,

"But, Joe, if all women wants is to be 'equal' to men then they'd be no better than us. There'd still be posh women, just like there be posh men, and poor women like there be poor fuckers like us? If we owns them turns to they owns us, what good would it be?"

"You're right, Watty, my dear old matey, that's the rub exactly. You canna blame 'em for wanting the vote and for pushing hard to get it but, if that's all they wants, then we're all still at the bottom of the hill.... We have to put our case to women and convince 'em that equality of the sexes won't get to the root of the problem, which is capitalism."

"There's something else though Joe", says Watty with a

glint in his eye, "Being as women are getting organised, politically so to speak, then we can make good use of the fact...we have to join up with 'em but that's a dam sight easier now they're on the march anyway!"

James Keir Hardie died on the 25th September 1915, a broken man, ostracised by many of his friends and comrades, partly because of his support for women's suffrage but mainly because of his anti-war position. The war triggered many dramatic events across Europe and beyond. On Easter Monday 1916, large parts of Dublin were seized and a Republic declared. Mary Harmison's mother, Catherine, had been to Dublin and stood on a bridge looking down at the River Liffey. She had often talked of the beauties of Sackville Street to Mary but would have rejoiced at their destruction by the so-called rebels. She had stayed with her cousin who worked at Jacob's biscuit factory also taken over by the rebels. In October 1917, Russia's Winter Palace was 'stormed', although the assumption of power by the Bolsheviks was largely un-resisted. A force of Cossacks and a female regiment were quickly routed. Russia was such a long way away that folk on the Clee Hills had little knowledge of these momentous events that would soon change the world. Marx's ideas were to be put into practice for the first time and, although they were often misused, ninety years later the people of Cuba still reap the benefits, having the same average lifespan as folks in the much richer USA. There is so much more that could be said about the significance of Marxism but, for now, we must press on with our story.

It's a warm Saturday evening in the summer of 1919. The war is done, perhaps better to say that the fighting is over while the consequences, in terms of bereavement and nursing wounds, continue to bite. Mary and Sarah Mann are talking with a now white-haired Catherine Watson (Albert's wife) and a younger

Lottie Thread in the Mann's back garden. The men, as per usual, are at the pub after a football match played against one of the rival village teams. The topic of the women's conversation is getting hit by their husbands.

"Watty's never laid a finger on me, though if he did I should wait my moment before cracking him 'cross the snout with the poker for his trouble, or worse if 'nd I've a mind to," says Mary with a knowing twinkle in her eye.

"You've been lucky, Mary, I've had some bad moments with Bert," answers Lottie.

Mary changes her expression to serious,

"And your Joe, Cath, we used to hear you both flarin' up and then there'd be a squawking…you used to say you both had to take refuge and hide under the kitchen table.."

"That was right. But, he's not a bad man…at heart. I think he rages inside about his leg that has held him back all his life. Still, it was Will who had to put a stop to it. One night Joe was back early, he'd had a skin-full, boozed up on cider and whiskey…he starts his antics, laying into me and Will, knuckles not slapping, and Will barely fifteen years of age at the time….like he'd always done. Anyways, Will takes hold of him by the muffler and marches him outside, bolts the door and lets him go mad, banging, kicking and calling to the devil…Once he cooled down, Will let him back in but told him that the same course of action would be taken at the hint of any further nonsense."

"But men has the final say mother," says Sarah, "'cos you have to rely on Will to keep Joe civil when he's had a few too many, which is pretty often."

"Well, that's the way it should be…otherwise you would be going against nature", offers Lottie, "men has the say-so for a reason, it is the natural way of things."

Mary's face shows her annoyance,

"Even if that was ever the truth Lottie, such matters are changing, don't you think? Since the war ended all of us sitting here has got the vote and even our first MP, if she ever gets out of Holloway Gaol she'll be sitting amongst the men in the House of Commons."

"We have to be aged thirty years or more while men can be twenty one, so's it's not level yet. If it was, we women would have the whip-hand, given as so many men was killed in the war. But men are a daft breed. If I was twenty one and well-to-do, I could get elected to be an MP even though I couldna' vote. Only men could manage such a concoction!"

"I read it in the Herald that our Constance will never take her seat, on principle," says Catherine who is the only one of the four who can read a newspaper."

Lottie hits back,

"And a good thing too....she was a German spy, so folk says, married to a foreign Count and a gaol-bird to boot. She was one of the ringleaders for the Irish rising when we was busy fighting the Kaiser."

The clock speeds up again, dear reader. It is now 1930 and the funeral for Catherine Watson has just taken place. She has died, aged seventy-two years, from skin cancer, worn out, a frail white-haired old lady, so unlike the feisty woman she had been in her prime. Walter's youngest daughter, Mary Mann, had tended her to the last. The smell of her disease had been so bad that Joe had taken coal embers from the fire to the bottom of the stairs and let the smoke do its work. Caroline Mann, Sarah, now married and living in Liverpool, and Maggie Claverley, a friend of Catherine's from Worcester, are walking towards the bonk, getting some air and a break from the sandwiches. It's a cold but sunny, early spring afternoon. Will Mantle and one of the Haynes' boys are racing down the sheep-tracks. A lone carrion crow watches their antics intently, waiting patiently to re-visit the remains of a vixen shot by one of the squire's gamekeepers.

"How are things Sarah? I hear your Ernie's working in the docks, on the banana boats,

"We're getting by, Carrie, getting by. Young Ernie's working on the same gang and they're both tipping up their money every week so I'm not about to complain. Mind you, they're coming home stinking from sweat and filth…and young Ern' brought a bloody great spider home last week, big as a dinner plate and hairy, makes me shiver to think of it…men are working in the holds of them boats and such animals are loose down there, gives me nightmares..."

"Changing the subject, Sarah, I can't abide such crawlin' things, what do you make of Mr Ramsay McDonald so far? Another Labour government, thanks be to God, and we've a handful of women MPs. And nows we can vote on the same footing as the men, I've a spring in my step..I wish Cath was still alive, just to see it!"

"They're a well-heeled bunch though, Carrie, fancy Lady this and fancy Lady that....I doubt if any of 'em would recognise the kind of life we 'as grubbing along the bottom to make a penny.."

"True as a daisy....when you think upon what Cath went through…she was in bad pain towards the end…but still the doctor wouldna come…Joe had to walk the four miles and back each time to buy the morphine. Them lot wants a proper sortin' out, that's what it boils down to.."

The women begin to make their return with the sun dropping fast and the first signs of redness edging the high cloud,

"I heard that one of 'em was from our class, Brimfield, I think it was, Margaret, Maggie Brimfield...she's the one who Ramsay has promoted...she's the first ever Minister, I believes."

"I don't know Carrie, I don't know...I can recall the first woman MP, for our party, the Lawrence woman in London...then there was Dorothy Jewson, in 1924, I remembers the date due to it being the year young William Mantle was born...that's him running the sheep ragged over toward the lone Scots pine...do you see him? He's the blond boy with the boots many sizes too big for his feet....You knows the family Maggs, Mary's boy...they moved back up from Ludla....Will Mantle and Mary's eldest boy. He's a nice lad'll do anything for ya. They cum up to Speke to see us last year, Will working on the Great Western and getting a rail pass once a year to New Brighton, that's how they could afford it."

They arrive back at Titterstone cottages, wood smoke coming steady from the Mann's chimney.

"Walter's burning the mattress by the smell of it!" says Maggie, not thinking.

"No, he's done that earlier", replies Caroline quietly, a tear in the corner of her eye.

They reach the front path, strewn with twigs. Watty opens the door and beckons the women to get a shift on. He is holding the end of a tree trunk.

"I see you've got the kindling in, Watty!" jests Lottie.

"Why not tell everybody outright," replies the Biscuit, with a scowl, before taking the tree out through the back door for chopping up.

Fire-wood was a valuable commodity on the Clee Hills, being such a bleak, wind-swept place over the winter months. Most of the trees were gnarled old hawthorns or mountain ash, kept small by the elements. Watty had spotted a pile of felled timber in one of the squire's copses. He would normally have moved the wood at night but had been tipped off that it was to be keenly watched after dusk. The tree would be converted quickly into logs and distributed amongst the widows, sick and elderly in the row of cottages.

Observing Watty and his daughter Caroline, anyone with half an eye would have noticed a certain tension. This dated back to an event when Caroline was a youngster, something for which she had never forgiven her father. It was still paining her to recall. She had come to the front door holding the family sugar bowl, just a cheap old thing but hard to replace, nevertheless. Watty, approaching the cottage, shouts at her not to drop it which she, as if to cue, proceeds to do. In a flash of temper, he removes his belt and strikes Caroline, hard, with the buckle. While she had always been fearful, from that moment, Caroline lost much of her respect for her father. True, in those times, children were 'seen and not heard' and it was far from unusual for violence to be used by parents when they stepped out of line, as children inevitably do. For Caroline, this did not matter a jot. Watty was her father and he had used his physical power against her. This could not be undone. A telling off or slap would have been sufficient, coming from him, being so big and strong, as he was.

As Watty works hard on the tree in the backyard with axe and saw, the two sisters, Caroline and Sarah, share their memories, standing in the hall and taking care that their father does not hear.

"I can't forgive or forget it, Sarah, I've tried but I can't", says Caroline. "Times was hard and I know that he was only doing what most fathers would do but I cunna forget it."

"To be truthful Carrie, he never so much as put a finger on me....mind you, I was always too scared of 'im. I was too frightened to put a foot wrong or ever answer him back for fear of what I'd get for my trouble. He's such a big man and a temper to match it. To be honest, I'm not sure which is worst, the hiding or the fear of it."

"Neither's all that pretty, Sarah, nor welcome, nor necessary in these days of progress. But, think on what some men does. There was the Ringley lad, you remembers don't ya? They lives down at Bitterley. She's old Mrs Smith's youngest daughter…Very dark hair…His step-dad beat him black 'n blue with a fish-board…put him in bed for a week. And just for taking a few coppers off the mantelpiece. They say he near killed the poor lad and would have done but for being dragged off by the boy's uncles."

"A bad business that was indeed. But he was a squirt of a man and small men sometimes feels like they has to act up…"

"Like a puffed up bantam cock!"

"That's right, like a struttin' cock", says Sarah, a giggling smile across her face, "an upright dick, if you likes…"

"Do you think he ever did it…the hitting I means… to anybody else in the family", Carrie interjects, trying to shift the direction of conversation. "I don't recall seeing him ever strike mother…nor the boys for that matter? Having said that, there was times when the twins had been up to their mischief and sent off to bed early with a flea in their ears. I can't hardly recall…"

"You expect it more with boys though", answers Sarah, back in serious mode, picking at a loose piece of wood on the fence and getting a splinter for her reward.

"No child should have to endure it, Sarah, 'specially a young girl but even boys should be free of it…I'm not saying there should be no discipline nor punishments but they should be kept to the least possible."

As Watty completes his sawing, the two young women swiftly change the subject and walk out to the gate and, arm-in-arm, turn up the track towards Titterstone, well out of earshot,

"Perhaps it's time you told him what the trouble is, Carrie, 'stead of broodin' on it the way you have been doing. Just come out with it….I dunna suppose he'll do anything and I'm certain he knows something's not right between you both. If you picks your moment careful, maybes when I'm there as well, that might do the trick…."

"I'm not sure, Sarah, 'though that's a kind offer you're making and the idea makes every sense….I should be able to tell him, he's my father after all", Carrie mumbles unconvincingly. She never did tell him.

In the 1930s, the peak production period for Highley Colliery, a tunnel was built under the Severn to link up with the village of Alveley, in addition to the crossing known as 'Miners' Bridge'. This could take light motor vehicles and was the only public bridge for miles upstream or downstream. Just outside the village stands the buttercross, from the time of the Black Death in the 14th Century when provisions were left for the affected villagers to collect. Walter, by then in his late sixties, had made what would be his last trip from Titterstone to his birthplace in order to walk under the river. He timed it using his pocket-watch, secured by a long chain to his waistcoat, worn over his usual open-necked shirt, sleeves rolled up above the elbow, and strode slowly, as always, with his head high. More anxious souls let their fears dash ahead in the ill-lit shadows, water dripping, echoes and rats scampering. Walter was miles away with his thoughts. Overall, he had a sense of contentment but wished he could start again as a young man. He would be able to use his experience to push forward the cause. He would not be so fearful of powerful men. Trade unions had been held back by the bosses on the Clee Hills and Watty knew that he should have used his influence more to counter this. He would not be so pig-headed, more understanding and willing to listen even when he didn't agree. He was sorry for some of the things he had done while out at night poaching: he had to admit to himself that once or twice he'd used too much force in quietening gamekeepers and perhaps, as a younger man, even enjoyed it. He bitterly regretted having taken his belt to Caroline, his own daughter, when she dropped the sugar bowl. This would haunt him to the end.

Alone, high up on Titterstone, Watty is thinking on his use of violence. As he'd done many times before, he watches a crow boldly harassing a sparrow hawk and his mind slips back to childhood. Would he now identify more with the crow, with its courage in the face of certain death? Certainly, he had come a long way. He had become much better at controlling his temper, through experience and spending time with himself simply pondering about it. It had come up in his conversations with Joe, of course, mainly in terms of the hardships of life for working people, their lack of power and how this left them with little option but to rage. But why take it out on your own family, especially the little 'uns, this was what still puzzled Watty. He could recall how John, his own father, had taken the belt to him and the others on occasions. A back-hander, as well, now and again. Then, taking it back through the generations, passed down from father to son. Not only that because his mother had sometimes slapped him. Once she had given him such a wallop that he had ended up in the corner of the room. So, it was not just being handed down by the men of the family.

Watty went deeper, like a dog with a bone, pursuing his own weaknesses. What else had he been given and how would this square up with what Marx was saying about people? Something Joe had told him came to mind and he held on dear to it. One cold December day, they were out looking at the gypsy horses,

"There's no need to repeat it out loud what I say, Watty. When you does that it sounds as if you're looking down your nose at it, 'condescending' is the posh word for it...and you've no need to do it."

"Condescending...?"

"There you go again, saying out loud what I've just said to you… it's not just the words either, it's how you say 'em. There's a mocking edge to it.."

Watty was back at the gate in his mind, hearing Joe's words as if they were being spoken for the first time. There was something important here that he'd discounted all those years ago. A kernel of truth in it. He recalled how his son, John, one of the twins, had one evening told him about something he'd learned at school, how the teacher had told them about the sun never setting on the British Empire. Watty could hear himself, the sarcasm in how he had replied and how John went so quiet after he had previously been brimming over with enthusiasm. Then, from somewhere way back, he heard his own father, John, do it, using the same dismissive tone. "Con..da. send…in". Then back even further to distant memories of his granddad. Again, the same tone, putting the other person down. Hand-me-downs. His grandfather had been a mean man, selfish, never put his hand in his pocket unless he had to. Brought up by his grandmother, a 'granny-reared 'un', as was said on the Clee Hills. Perhaps, this was where it came from, the sarcasm? But, what would Marx say about it? How would it fit in with all the stuff about classes and such? He wished he could talk with Joe but he was living in Ludla nowadays with Mary and her family. All he could recall was that Marx had written about people being pressed down by their past...yes, that was it, as well as making history people were burdened by it and that growing up, as Joe used to say, was about getting a sense of our past, putting it in its place and getting on with building the future. He still wasn't totally sure but he was getting there, he thought.

But this was only half the story, Watty sensed. What was he missing out? Despite the competing chiff-chaff's and long-tailed titmouse's chatterings, he listened hard to himself. "The sins of the father afflict unto the several generations" came like an express train to mind, followed by, "The Lord God, a compassionate God, slow to anger..." Slow to anger! What the fuck was this? What happens when he does get bloody angry, given as he made the world in less than a week? Given as he made all the heavens and the earth in the dark! Then the penny drops and Watty's fizzog (face) bursts into a tickled smile of no mean proportion. "That's it! I'm full to the brim with clap-trap, forced into me when I was too young to know it for what it was! After all, I was just a little child so knew no different then but it's deep inside me now, accepted, even though I'm grown up. So when I starts to thinking about something it's like turning on a tap and out comes such pigwash! By that I means it's not connected, not 'logical' as Joe would say. But then there is something in "the sins of the father", that's what I'm trying to figure out, what I've taken on from my father and from his father. But there's also what I've taken on from other people, like churchmen and teachers. What was their purpose in doing it to me? Did they know what they was doing, anymore than I knows now? Was my schooling really about the truth at all? Was I brought up to be a poor labouring man? To have the thoughts, only, of a quarryman, fit to cut and load stone and that is all? So, that's how it matches up with what Marx was saying. It's personal to me but he's saying it happens to whole swathes of the population, fitting them ready for the mills, mines, fields and factories, like animals, beasts tethered, nothing more than that? And women too, perhaps even worse for women, tethered. I should have liked to have known much more about the world, not just machines...natural things like butterflies, birds, plants and trees, about which I am so ignorant. How the sun, stars, earth and moon came about, how they really came about as well, not the parson's baby talk. How the Clee Hills was made too, how they was formed and why they stands so tall and proud. How all them boulders got there. I should have been better educated, we all should, all us working people. None of us is so stupid that we canna be taught."

But there were good things too, Watty continued. "As far back as I can go, I always could feel sorry for people in trouble...and care for people struggling to make ends meet or sick and unable to fend for themselves...it's in my bones to do it. Like poor Brown, the workhouse boy. I cried for days to have him come home with me. And, Mrs Jackson, I worked hard for her, just to help. I never wanted anything in return for what I done neither. Not like some men would. As far as I can tell, I don't think I'm a bad man, least I hopes not. But was it important to care for my fellows so? And not just people. My mother always said I was soft on animals. That I cried when I saw any animal dead or when something had to be killed. When I was five, I bawled for hours over a hedgehog run over by a cart wheel. Not every kid does that. And I shouted at the knobs chasing foxes and closed the gates across the fields down near Henley to hold 'em up. Some folks can't see anything wrong in hounding poor animals for pleasure but I knew it was wrong, even as I little 'un. It's who I am and I hope I've always tried to do things for a good purpose".

Follow me now down the steep slopes and lanes that twist and tumble from Titterstone Cottages to Ludlow town. Mrs Temple is making her way from the Grange to her favourite tea-shop, via the riverside walk which abuts Steventon, a working class area of terraced homes and neat front gardens. Her thoughts are on Housman's A Shropshire Lad. "So silly to be so serious-minded in Spring" she says to herself, "just plain silly, life's too short". Then she is brought to an abrupt stop by what she sees in one of the terrace windows. Through the wooden front gate she turns, a few steps forward and a look of disdain crosses her powdered face, spotting the large ginger cat busy cleaning itself, leg up like a ballet-dancer, although Mr Temple always called it 'violin practice'. She straightens her own fur-lined collar, takes a deep breath and taps the door, which opens quickly because she'd been spotted coming down the road,

"Ah, Mrs Mantle...I was just passing by and noticed your advertisement for the Daily Herald newspaper.."

"Yes, it's my Will's, my husband Will's, what can I do for you?"

"Well, this is a delicate matter, of course, but I have to ask you to remove it from your window."

"I dunna think it's a bad paper...there's not a bit a harm in it..."

"Mrs Mantle, it is not the kind of thing that I wish to see in people's windows as I take my afternoon walk down to the river. I'm sure you would not know this but the editor of the paper is a communist and incites the labouring classes to expect too much and behave in ways well beyond their station."

"But Will's a skilled man, he works on the Great Western..."

"I assure you not for much longer if you leave that in your

window…now, Mary, do take what I say in the spirit that it is offered, I am trying to help you…you know how highly I regard the work you did for me last summer, our garden paving has never been so free of weeds…but you really must see sense on this matter, it is not something I can allow to be displayed in Ludlow….it is not the place for it…we can not, we simply will not have socialism in this town, whatever the cost, I'm afraid.. now, I really must be on my way to town so will bid you good-day."

As Mrs Temple abruptly shuts the gate, Mary can still feel the soreness of her knees and back caused by hours weeding at the Grange. She stares momentarily at her hands and her mind wanders round some of the other hurts she has had to endure throughout her life. The top of one of her fingers is missing. It was lost when she developed an infected wound, working in domestic service at Bacon's Farm, because the farmer refused to let her take time off to get medical treatment. It ended, thankfully, one day when Sarah came visiting and, hearing her sister's sorry plight, gave the farmer's wife a mouthful to remember before taking Mary home to Titterstone Cottages. But such physical pains are but pin-pricks compared with the hurt she feels at being addressed so rudely by someone for whom she had worked so long and diligently, making sure that every weed was pulled and every pathway swept pristine. Worse still is a hopelessness that presses down on her, in the knowledge that the paper will have to be removed. Taken down it will have to be, otherwise young Will, Jeff and Mary will be going without the little they presently get.

There were many other incidents of a similar nature, stories often re-told in families and communities about the way working people were regarded and so roughly treated. Will Mantle is a sailor on the RMS Arlanza, originally a liner, converted to an armed merchant cruiser during the First World War. He is on weekend leave from active service – blockade duty - near the Scandinavian coast. It is winter and Will's hands are still raw from hacking the ice off the ship's super-structure and decks. He is taking a shortcut across the fields to Titterstone, smartly dressed in his civvies. He meets Benton the fat-faced farmer,

"Now then lad, just hold there a minute!…you've a bloody nerve walking across my land, disturbing game and being out and about where you shouldn't…..what are you doing hanging around here anyway, why are you not away serving your country like your comrades? Get along with you."

Will continues his journey without a word. Benton attempts to block his way but slips on a dollop of fresh sheep shit, loose, smelly and dark green like a goose's. By the time he gets to his feet, Will has vaulted the stile. Later that evening at the pub Will is standing by the bar in his navy uniform, cap jaunty, set well back on his head. He is busy relating a story about German torpedoes speeding past the ship. Will is unable to swim but then only a minute or so in the icy cold water would be sufficient to finish a man so swimming would not count for all that much. Just then, in walks Benton, the same farmer, already boozed up and trousers changed, who spots Will, walks over and immediately becomes apologetic, offering to buy him a drink and saying he is welcome to walk the fields whenever he chooses, perhaps even take a rabbit or two. Again, Will maintains a dignified silence.

"Damn your eyes, then, sailor. I've put myself out enough. I will humble myself on your account no further. If I see you on my land again, expect a barrel or two of lead shot for your trouble!"

Watty is sitting silent in the corner, attentive to what is

transpiring but not giving anything away. He rises as if away for a leak while making his way round to the inn's frontage, where Benton is unsteadily making his way to horse and trap, hitched at the rail. Watty walks silently behind and deftly trips his man. Benton lands in his second helping of mammalian excrement for the day, this time of the steaming horse variety. Watty is back sitting inside with his crew before the fat farmer is up aiming wild fists at the night. Will is oblivious to what has taken place on his behalf and Watty has a poker face. Small moments of revenge in the interminable contest between the classes.

Walter died in 1947, aged 80, from cancer of the stomach. His parting shot, said with a smile and unrelated to his dying, was that the distribution of tinned pineapples during the war had prevented an uprising by the working classes. Amidst the fine carved stones and filigree metal left to remember members of the middle and upper classes, there is nothing to mark his churchyard grave. It's as if all his hard work in the quarries, mines and fields counted for nought and, of course, this is precisely what the machine of capitalism does to working class people. Similar things can be said for Mary, his wife, in terms of her lifetime of domestic labour and servitude spent in rich people's houses. People who don't have the brains they were born with will say that 'class' doesn't matter any longer. For me, it's not so much whether it matters because it goes much, much deeper than that. The closest I can get is to say that I 'am' my class, that this is the key to 'who I am'. There are a number of statements about my sense of identity which help to nail this idea down. First, I am not an individual soul seeking salvation, enlightenment, celebrity or my personal place in heaven. Just like Walter would say, such talk is plain silly, fit only for the nursery. 'Fetishism' would make an interesting, alternative descriptor for such notions. Second, I am not a unique, human 'personality' - I have much more in common with my fellows and, indeed, with individuals from the other species co-habiting our wonderful planet. I think that this is so, so important. We must stop victimising one another. Third, I am not defined in terms of my nationality. Again, childish talk, as well as a refuge for scoundrels. Similar negations could be listed for my gender, race, family, sexuality etcetera. The importance of every one of these apparent 'differences' swiftly disappears on close inspection. Finally, and this is really difficult, I have to learn how to move on from 'ownership'. I am custodian, not owner. Paying money for something or someone is a madness or sin, take your pick! Marx understood all of these things and, although I've often read his words and he died such a long time ago, it's taken a lifetime to grasp fully what he was about. There can be no doubt in my mind that he was a genius. Like Einstein, he could get to the root of even the most complex subjects and put over his ideas in a way that everyone, with a little effort, can understand. He was also fearless and, like all good scientists, able to resist the temptations of privilege and complacency in search of 'truth'. Let me leave you with one of his gems,

> *"The bourgeoisie has stripped of its halo every occupation hitherto honoured and looked up to with reverent awe. It has converted the physician, the lawyer, the priest, the poet, the man of science, into its paid wage-labourers"* (p.45).

as relevant for me, the author of this book, as it was for Walter, the quarryman, in his time. In a nutshell, Marx is saying that capital's ascendancy sucks out everything good from people's work. Some will relate these changes to 'globalisation'. Some will portray them as inevitable, as the world economy arrives. Others, of more suspect morals, will be glad of capitalism's dominance. Of course, there is probably little that could be done to shift their minds. This book, though, is especially dedicated to two groups of readers. First, working class people who have been reared to spend their lives without being conscious of class and, second, those older souls who have once known its significance but since lost their way. As a reminder to both groups of how damaging capitalism continues to be, more than three quarters of poor children in the UK fail to achieve even five decent GCSE passes, the minimum necessary for a successful, healthy life. The book's conclusion is that the current system, just like the one operating in Walter's childhood, cannot provide an environment fit to raise our children in and that it, therefore, must be replaced. How to do this is, of course, immensely difficult but a number of ways to inch ourselves forward come to mind. For sure, alternative employment will have to be found for profiteers, spivs and their assorted lackeys but, most importantly, we have to organise ourselves again. Organise ourselves around a future that will be worthwhile for everyone - as the Manifesto states, organise ourselves in such a way that the present comes to dominate the past, rather then the other way round (p.65). It's as simple and as perplexing as that. We have to put aside infantile ideas of nation, religion, kings and queens, race, culture and other well-polished props for capitalism. Little coincidence that such pap exists alongside the sham of present-day 'democracy' which periodically exchanges one set of capitalists for another. No surprises either about the public apathy towards and woeful ignorance of science. Finally, we have to push hard together for a world where each one of us gives and receives care and support - we have to stop grinding each other into the dirt.

References

Chevalier, T. (2001) Falling Angels, London: Harper.

Chown, M. (2006) Quantum Theory Cannot Hurt You: A Guide to the Universe, London: Faber and Faber.

Marx, K. and Engels, F. (1975) Manifesto of the Communist Party, Moscow: Progress (reproduced from Samuel Moore's 1888 translation of the original German text of 1848).

Watts, W.W. (1919) Shropshire: The Geography of the County, Shrewsbury: Wilding & Son.

Lightning Source UK Ltd.
Milton Keynes UK
09 January 2010

148300UK00001B/3/P